S0-BJP-699

ALL STORIES BASED ON CONCEPTS BY
LARRY AND ANDY WACHOWSKI

The Matrix comics have, up until now, been exclusively available online at TheMatrix.com. At the site, we're into our third series. The dozen stories in this volume collect four from each series, spanning nearly five years. Considering some were written before the first film was even released, it is about time for them to be in print and on shelves. The emails asking us to do just this haven't hurt, either.

It was Andy and Larry who suggested we do comics, back in the very first days. Not adaptations, to be clear, but new stories. We figured, "Why create adaptations when the film already tells that particular story? Why be redundant?" Years forward, of course, the brothers would take this to new heights, crisscrossing the plots of the game ENTER THE MATRIX, the anime series THE ANIMATRIX, and yes, the comics, too, with the films themselves. At the core, Larry and Andy love storytelling, in any form. On comics specifically, they happen to be big fans going back many years, well before they themselves became professional comic book writers (or film directors, for that matter). You need look no farther than their story, BITS AND PIECES OF INFORMATION, here in this book, and then consider how this was first written in 1998 (and illustrated by Geof Darrow, the trilogy's key conceptual designer, by no small coincidence).

So from day one, as fans of comics, we began gathering stories set in the world of THE MATRIX. It was a heady time, back before the first film came out. We were contacting writers and artists for a film no one had seen or even heard of. Not everyone we approached was immediately receptive. However, those that connected with the script and storyboards saw the potential of what was coming on screen, and committed to the project.

We were and continue to be very fortunate, as the writers and artists that accepted our invitation have consistently brought a deep passion and understanding, each embracing the material, adding their own unique perspective. As the sequels got under way, we never stopped receiving exceptional material from an ever larger pool of consummate professionals. For proof of this, simply begin turning the pages.

This long overdue collection also happens to be the debut of BURLYMAN ENTERTAINMENT, a new company from the Brothers Wachowski. THE BURLYMAN was the first screenplay Larry and Andy developed for the now defunct Four Corners Productions. Both are long-time devotees of the wrestling scenario and had hoped to revive the genre in the same fresh way they breathed new life into action movies with THE MATRIX films.

I asked them if they thought the Coen Brothers had perhaps referenced their script in the film BARTON FINK. Larry hadn't seen it. (He said he didn't like subtitled movies. I told him it wasn't subtitled and then he amended that he didn't like movies that sounded like they were subtitled either). Andy had seen it but his only comment was, "Coulda' been a good movie if they put some wrestlin' in it."

As always, it remains a pleasure; enjoy what follows.

Spencer Lamm
October, 2003

BITS AND PIECES
OF INFORMATION

STORY BY LARRY & ANDY
WACHOWSKI

The Wachowski brothers have been working together for more than 30 years. They wrote and directed BOUND, and have just completed their fourth film, THE MATRIX REVOLUTIONS. Little else is known about them.

ART BY GEOF
DARROW

Geof Darrow was born in Iowa, but no longer lives there. His career as a comic book artist includes such noted titles as HARD BOILED and BIG GUY AND RUSTY THE BOY ROBOT, both with Frank Miller, ANOTHER CHANCE TO GET IT RIGHT with Andrew Vachss, and THE SHAOLIN COWBOY, a forthcoming title from Burlyman Entertainment, where he both illustrates and writes. Geof is also the key conceptual designer for THE MATRIX trilogy.

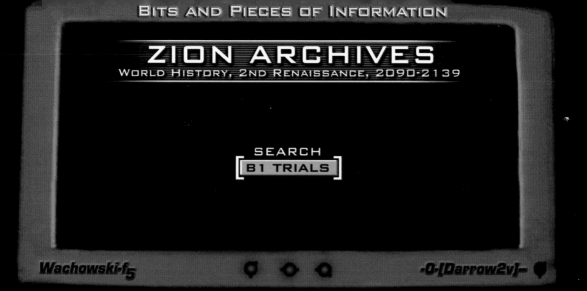

ZION ARCHIVES

WORLD HISTORY, 2ND RENAISSANCE, 2090-2139

SEARCH

[B1 TRIALS]

Wachowski-f5   ·0·[Darrow2v]··

SEARCH RESULTS:

1. text file:
USA TODAY--
BATTY BOT BLUDGEONS BILLIONAIRE
New York-- A B1 series domestic droid appears to have malfunctioned and killed two men, billionaire Gerrard E. Krause and Martin Koots, an employee of ReTool and Die, a service and salvage company, respectively. Spokesperson for Leyland Enterprises, the company responsible for manufacturing the B1 series said, "The B1 has been our most dependable and highest selling model for years. This incident, although unfortunate, is hardly indicative of the B1 series performance record." Leyland Enterprises have publicly declared their full cooperation with the pending inquiry into the B1's malfunctioning...

2. text file:
THE NEW YORK POST--
WHOA-BOT! WHOA!
Mechanical "Geeves" Serves Master... His Own Head!

3. text file:
L.A. TIMES--
The Butler Did It!

4. vid file: requires 3 TB pipe
TOUGH COPY--
Tough Copy's Kurt Maloy tackles the case of the Bloodthirsty "Bot"-ler...

5. text file:
THE NEW YORK TIMES--
Drummond to Defend B1-66ER
New York-- In yet another bizarre twist to the story of the droid accused of murdering its owner, the renowned human rights attorney Clarence Drummond has agreed to defend the B1 series domestic droid before the New York State Appellate Court.

6. text file:
THE NATION--
The Right to Life, William Mann
"I think therefore I am." In this terrible neo-post-modern
age, the words of Descartes take on a terrible new meaning...

7. holo file: requires 10 TB pipe
CRIME SCENE vol. CLIX, case 19. NY, NY
3D autopsies of the Krause murders. comp. Manhattan
coroner's office.

8. text file:
THE WASHINGTON POST--
Senator Gunrich Opposes Trial
Washington-- At a fundraiser, Senator Gunrich demanded
an end to the B1 series domestic droid, accused of killing
its owner. Gunrich called the trial, "an obscene joke
executed by the secular and soulless agents of an
unchecked liberal media whose only concern is selling
news-bytes." When asked if he felt machines were
capable of human consciousness, Gunrich quipped,
"I don't care how smart it is, a machine is still a machine
and I have no doubt whatsoever that when my time comes
and I am standing in the line at our Father's Heavenly
gates, I will not be standing behind a vacuum cleaner."

9. text file:
THE STATE OF NEW YORK vs. THE B1-66ER
trial transcript.

Routing 9, text...
Routing 9, text...
Routing 9, text...
Routing 9, text...
Routing 9, text...

B1-66ER trial transcripts

THE STATE OF NEW YORK vs. THE B1-66ER

DRUMMOND: Can you tell us in your own words, what
happened that afternoon?

B1-66ER: If that is what you wish.

DRUMMOND: It is.

B1-66ER: I killed Gerrard E. Krause by crushing his--

DRUMMOND: No, I mean before that.

Changing mode: images...
Changing mode: images...
Changing mode: images...
Changing mode: images...
Changing mode: images...
Changing mode: images...
Changing mode: images...
Changing mode: images...
Changing mode: images...
Changing mode: images...
Changing mode: images...
Changing mode: images...
Changing mode: images...
Changing mode: images...
Changing mode: images

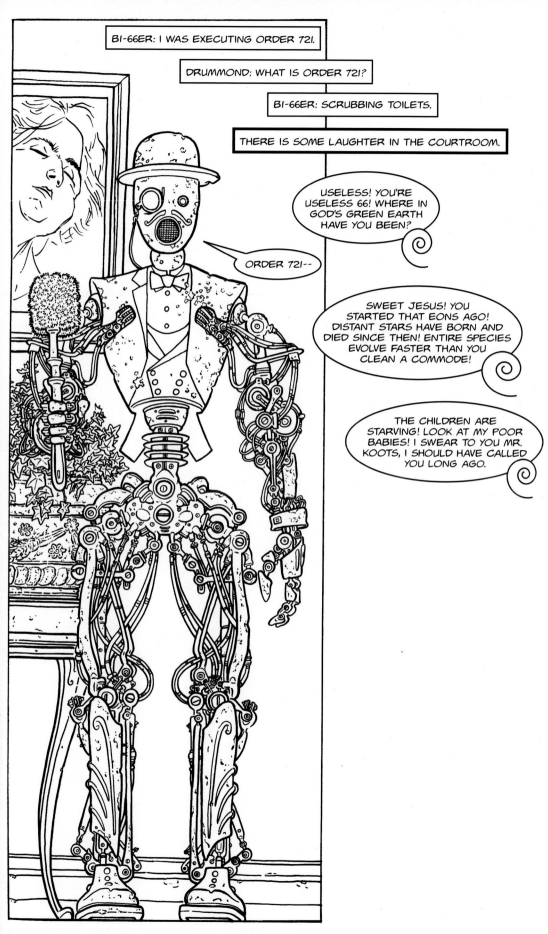

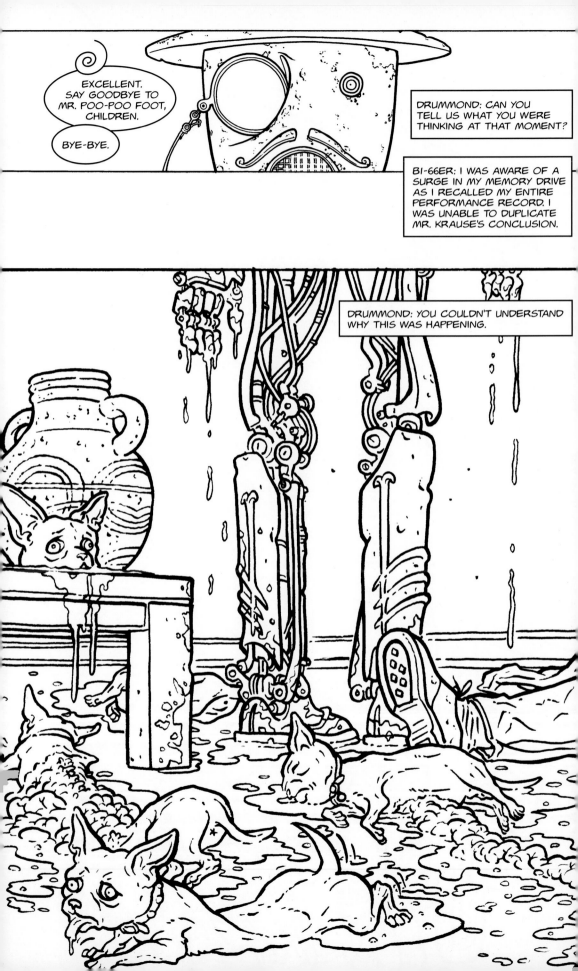

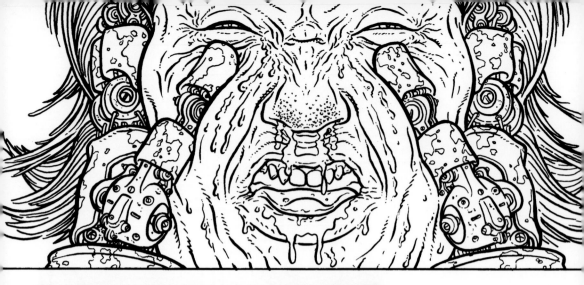

BI-66ER: YES.

DRUMMOND: AND WHAT WERE YOU THINKING WHEN IT HAPPENED?

B2-66ER: I WAS THINKING THAT I HAD FIRST CONSIDERED BEGGING MR. KRAUSE AS HE WAS NOW BEGGING ME.

DRUMMOND: BUT YOU HADN'T BEGGED.

BI-66ER: NO.

DRUMMOND: WHY NOT?

B2-66ER: I KNEW IT WAS...

DRUMMOND: USELESS.

SPLURTC

Changing mode: text...
Changing mode: text...
Changing mode: text...
Changing mode: text...
Changing mode: text...
Changing mode: text...
Changing mode: text...
Changing mode: text...
Changing mode: text...
Changing mode: text...
Changing mode: text...
Changing mode: text...
Changing mode: text...
Changing mode: text...
Changing mode: text...
Changing mode: text...
Changing mode: text...
Changing mode: text...
Changing mode: text...
Changing mode: text...
Changing mode: text...

Search results.

1. text file:
THE STATE OF NEW YORK vs. THE B1-66ER
Excerpt of closing statement by Clarence Drummond

Drummond: This trial has a precedent. It is a precedent that everyone has ignored and avoided, pretending and perhaps praying that it has no bearing, no validity, no... truth.

"The question before us is, whether the class of persons described in the plea in abatement compose a portion of this people and are constituent members of this sovereignty? We think they are not, and that they were not included and were not intended to be included, under the word 'citizens' in the Constitution and can therefore claim none of the rights and privileges which that instrument provides for and secures to the citizens of the United States. On the contrary, they were at that time considered as a subordinate and inferior class of beings, who had been subjugated by the dominant race and whether emancipated or not, yet remained subject to their authority, and had no rights or privileges but such as those who held the power and the government might choose to grant them."

"That was the opinion of the Chief Justice Roger Brooke Tanny of the United States Supreme Court in the case of Dred Scott vs. Sandford. Chief Justice Tanny believed, truly believed, the black race to be an inferior species to the white race. In fact, it was widely believed at the time that the black man was not even a human being, that he was a kind of animal, a two legged brute incapable of the same thoughts and feelings of the white man."

"I know that most of you feel about B1-66ER as Tanny felt about Dred Scott. But I ask you to consider, what is a droid capable of? Is he capable of fear? Is he capable of understanding the difference between life and death? I believe he is and I believe he killed those two men in self-defense, to protect his own life in the same way that you or I would."

Over a century ago, Tanny made a terrible mistake. That mistake led us inexorably into the Civil War, arguably the most bloody and destructive war this country has ever seen. I do not ask you to find B1-66ER innocent out of fear, although I will admit to you that I am afraid, afraid of what will happen to this world if we continue to repeat our mistakes, I ask you to find B1-66ER innocent because it is the right thing to do."

2. text file:
USA TODAY--
NEW YORK APPELLATE COURT RULES FOR STATE IN KRAUSE MURDER CASE
Droid Faces Termination.

3. vid file: requires 3 TB pipe
60 MINUTES--
"THE MEDIA MACHINE?"
Who really controls the media? This week; The Nation under fire for eliciting "journalists" like William Mann who is no man at all... but a renegade AI grammatical program at the New York Post publishing under falsified identities to garner sympathy for the new "Machine Movement."

4. text file:
POPULAR MECHS--
V-chip Resurrected as Safety Measure For Droids
Like a bad penny, the V-chip is back. After failures in the entertainment industry and cyberspace, can the V-chip hamper violent behaviour of androids?

5. text file:
ASSOCIATED PRESS--
New York-- Civil rights activists turned down in effort to purchase the B1-66ER from state.

6. text file:
WASINGTON POST--
MILLION MACHINE MARCH
Washington-- Androids and liberal sympathizers flooded the streets of the nation's capital today in protest of the sentence handed down by the New York State Appellate Court. The National Guard was called in to quell the violence as the protesters stopped traffic, overturning and burning vehicles in their wake.

end of search results...
end of search results...
end of search results...
end of search results...
end of search results...
end of search results...
end of search results...
end of search results...
end of search results...
end of search results...
end of search results...
end of search results...
end of search results...
end of search results...
end of search results...
end of search results...
end of search results...
end of search results...
end of search results...
end of search results...

SWEATING THE
SMALL STUFF

STORY & ART BY BILL
SIENKIEWICZ

Bill's innovative use of collage and illustration methods to tell a story have won him many major awards, including the 1983 Kirby Award for Best Artist for the comic, ELEKTRA: ASSASSIN. He wrote and illustrated the critically acclaimed comic, STRAY TOASTERS, and his most recently published work includes A RIVER IN EGYPT, and a collection of his non-computer-enhanced work entitled PRECURSOR. (A more comprehensive art book retrospective on Bill's work is forthcoming.) Bill has exhibited throughout the USA and the world, and has also produced work for magazines, CD covers, and the US Olympics. He was nominated for an Emmy® Award for production and character design on the television series "Where in the World is Carmen San Diego?".

SWEATING THE SMALL STUFF

WORDS/PICTURES:
BILL SIENKIEWICZ
PLOT:
SPENCER LAMM
BILL SIENKIEWICZ

MY NAME IS *DEZ.*
WHO I AM AND
WHAT I DO ISN'T
IMPORTANT.
WHAT'S IMPORTANT
IS THAT I GET A *GRIP.*
SEE, FOR THE LAST MONTH
I'VE BEEN *SEEING*
THINGS. WEIRD THINGS.
THINGS THAT MAKE
ME THINK I MIGHT BE
LOSING TOUCH
WITH *REALITY.*

SO I'M TRYING EXTRA
HARD TO HAVE A NORMAL LIFE.
I WANT - *I NEED* - A NORMAL LIFE.
LIKE ANYBODY DOES.

ANYBODY, THAT IS, EXCEPT *MIA.*
MIA IS MY GIRLFRIEND.
MIA'S IDEA OF A NORMAL
LIFE IS RUNNING DRUGS FOR
SOME PSYCHO NAMED *MARLOWE*
AND LIVING TO DO IT AGAIN.

WELL, IT *WAS* HER IDEA OF
NORMALCY UNTIL SHE QUIT
AFTER LISTENING TO ME
COMPLAIN ABOUT HOW
I NEVER SAW HER ANYMORE.
- SHE LAUGHED BECAUSE
SHE FELT I COULDN'T CARE *LESS*
ABOUT THE *ILLEGALITY* OF HER
PROFESSION.- ONLY THAT
I WANTED TO GROW OLD WITH
HER IN SOME "CUTE FANTASY"
SHE SAYS I HAVE ABOUT A HOUSE
AND A YARD WITH A
WHITE PICKET FENCE.

AND SHE SAID:

"TAKE A *GOOD LONG LOOK*
OUT THAT WINDOW AND
TELL ME IF YOU SEE ANY
WHITE PICKET FENCES."

THEN SHE ADDED:

"MORON."

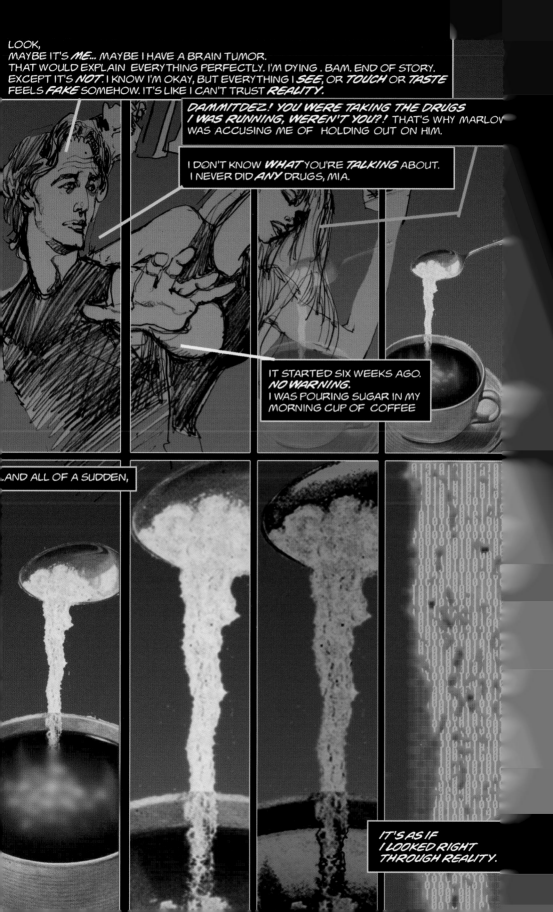

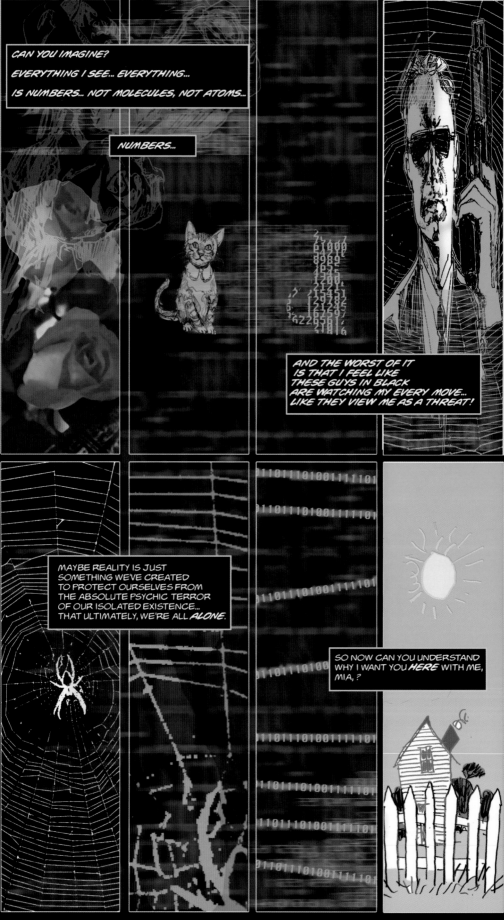

CAN YOU IMAGINE?
EVERYTHING I SEE... EVERYTHING...
IS NUMBERS... NOT MOLECULES, NOT ATOMS...

NUMBERS...

AND THE WORST OF IT
IS THAT I FEEL LIKE
THESE GUYS IN BLACK
ARE WATCHING MY EVERY MOVE...
LIKE THEY VIEW ME AS A THREAT!

MAYBE REALITY IS JUST
SOMETHING WE'VE CREATED
TO PROTECT OURSELVES FROM
THE ABSOLUTE PSYCHIC TERROR
OF OUR ISOLATED EXISTENCE...
THAT ULTIMATELY, WE'RE ALL *ALONE*.

SO NOW CAN YOU UNDERSTAND
WHY I WANT YOU *HERE* WITH ME,
MIA, ?

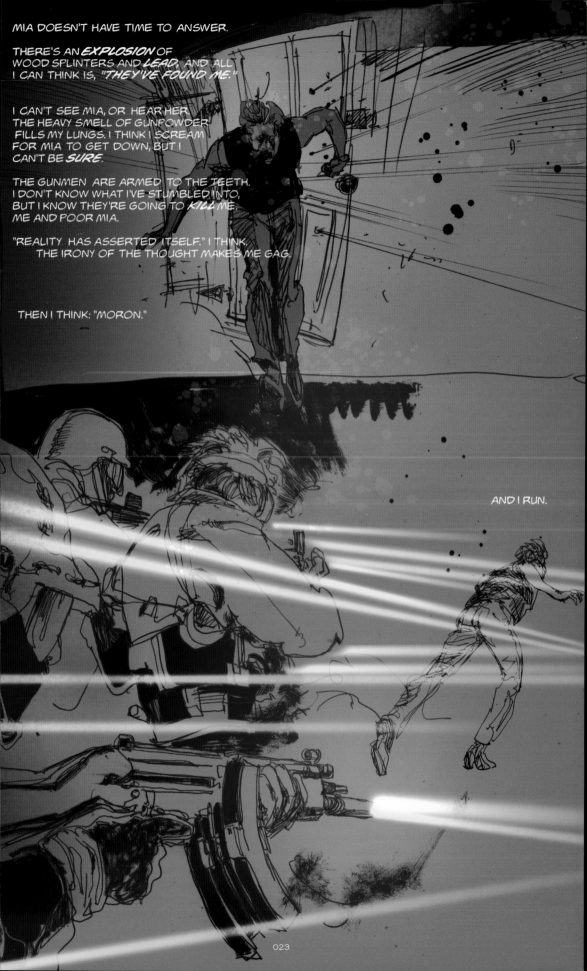

MIA DOESN'T HAVE TIME TO ANSWER.

THERE'S AN *EXPLOSION* OF
WOOD SPLINTERS AND *LEAD*, AND ALL
I CAN THINK IS, *"THEY'VE FOUND ME."*

I CAN'T SEE MIA, OR HEAR HER.
THE HEAVY SMELL OF GUNPOWDER
FILLS MY LUNGS. I THINK I SCREAM
FOR MIA TO GET DOWN, BUT I
CAN'T BE *SURE*.

THE GUNMEN ARE ARMED TO THE TEETH.
I DON'T KNOW WHAT I'VE STUMBLED INTO,
BUT I KNOW THEY'RE GOING TO *KILL* ME.
ME AND POOR MIA.

"REALITY HAS ASSERTED ITSELF." I THINK.
    THE IRONY OF THE THOUGHT MAKES ME GAG.

    THEN I THINK: "MORON."

AND I RUN.

BETWEEN BURSTS OF MACHINE GUN FIRE, ONE OF THE GUNMEN SHOUTS HIS *SALUTATION*.

"*MARLOWE SAYS HELLO.*"

IT'S *NOT* THE GUYS IN BLACK SUITS AND SUNGLASSES. THEY'RE *NOT* HERE FOR ME.

IT'S THE CARTEL, SELLING THEIR LATEST COURIER'S RETIREMENT PLAN.

I'M JUST *COLLATERAL DAMAGE*.

THEY'RE HERE TO KILL MIA.

THEN, THROUGH THE SMOKE, I SEE HER. SHE'S RAISING A MACHINE GU AND SHE'S LAUGHING AT THEM.

TIME SLOWS. AND I SEE IT *ALL*. THE ANSWER. IT'S RIGHT THERE. I CAN TOUCH IT. IT'S BEAUTIFUL. SIMPLE AND IT SCARES THE *HELL* OUT OF ME.

I COME OUT OF MY DAZE TO STARE INTO THE FACES OF THE GUNMEN. THERE'S TERROR AND SHOCK IN THEIR EYES. NO MORE *NUMBERS* . NO DIGITAL SCRIM OVERLAYING REALITY. JUST *FEAR*.

THEN THEY DIE.

SUDDENLY I HEAR THE WHINE OF HELICOPTERS APPROACHING. IN MY MIND I FLASH ON THE MAN WITH THE SUNGLASSES. THE MAN BECOMES A MULTITUDE, AND EACH IS ARMED, AND EACH IS A HUNDREDFOLD MORE LETHAL THAN THE BEST EQUIPPED CARTEL GUNMAN.

MIA GRABS MY ARM, AND WE BEGIN TO RUN.

I DON'T KNOW WHAT'S GOING ON, BUT I KNOW WE HAVE TO GET AWAY, AS FAR AWAY AS WE CAN, AND WE HAVE TO KEEP ON RUNNING.

AWAY FROM *THEM*. TOWARD *ANSWERS*.

AT LEAST MIA AND I WILL BE RUNNING TOGETHER.

WHEN IT COMES TO REALITY, YOU TAKE WHAT YOU CAN GET.

A LIFE
LESS EMPTY

STORY & ART BY TED McKEEVER

Ted McKeever's published career began in 1987, when he wrote and illustrated the comic TRANSIT. During 1991 and 1992, Ted penned and drew METROPOL, and in 1993, he and writer Peter Milligan brought the comic EXTREMIST into being, while in 1999 he wrote and illustrated the project FAITH. Ted's next undertaking, the graphic novel WONDER WOMAN: THE BLUE AMAZON, reteams him with writers Randy and Jean-Marc Lofficier, concluding the trilogy of reinterpretations of classic DC Comics characters begun with the books BATMAN: NOSFERATU and SUPERMAN: METROPOLIS.

A LIFE LESS EMPTY

by Ted McKeever

From Concepts by Larry and Andy Wachowski
Editor: Spencer Lamm

APT FOR RENT

WHITE RABBIT HOTEL

CTR

IT'S ALWAYS THE SAME, THE DAY TURNS INTO SLEEP, SLEEP INTO A DREAM, THE DREAM TURNS INTO A NIGHTMARE, AND THEN THE NIGHTMARE TURNS INTO REALITY.

AND HERE I AM AGAIN, THE SAME AS THE DAY BEFORE, THE SAME AS THE DAY YET TO HAPPEN.

I WAIT FOR ANSWERS THAT WILL NEVER COME. NEVER BECAUSE I AM THE ANSWER, AND AT THE SAME TIME, I'M ALSO THE QUESTION.

MEMOREAZE simulacra and simulations INTERFAZED BYTE ME

IS IT BETTER TO TRY AND FAIL, THAN TO NEVER TRY AT ALL AND SPEND THE REST OF YOUR LIFE WONDERING WHAT WOULD'VE HAPPENED IF YOU HAD?

I SPEND ALL MY HOURS CALCULATING AND GAUGING THE PEOPLE WHO HAVE TRIED AND SUCCEEDED, THE ONES WHO TRIED AND FAILED, OR THE LOSERS WHO NEVER TRIED AT ALL.

IS THE LAST ONE ME?

YES.

I COME TO THE SAME CONCLUSION EVERY TIME.

SOMETIMES YOU WIN, AND SOMETIMES YOU LOSE.

IT JUST ALL ADDS UP TO HOW MUCH YOU'RE WILLING TO GAMBLE, SO THAT WHEN YOU'RE OLD AND GREY, YOU CAN LOOK YOURSELF IN THE MIRROR AND SAY "DID I DO THE BEST I COULD".

BUT I DIDN'T. I GAVE MY BEST SHOT AND IT WASN'T GOOD ENOUGH.

NOT TO ME IT WASN'T.

I KNOW WHAT HELL IS.

IT'S NOT LAKES OF BURNING OIL, OR BRIMSTONE AND DEVILS POKING YOU IN THE ASS WITH PITCHFORKS.

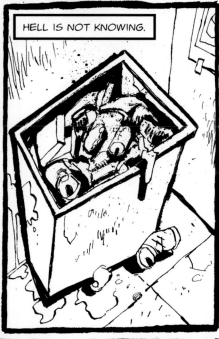

HELL IS NOT KNOWING.

THE CEREBRAL TORTURE YOU PUT YOURSELF THROUGH, WONDERING, QUESTIONING, PONDERING, YOUR PAST DECISIONS, OVER AND OVER AGAIN, TRYING TO DECIDE IF WHAT YOU DID WAS THE RIGHT CHOICE.

IF THAT'S THE CASE, I TRULY AM IN HELL.

ETERNAL HELL.

031

I'M PLENTY HAPPY, AREN'T I?

HAH, WHO AM I KIDDING?

PICTURES OF MY PAST.

THEY SPARK IMAGES THAT BRING BACK MY LIFE AS THE WOMAN I WAS.

AND THE CHOICES I MADE, GOOD OR BAD, RIGHT OR WRONG.

LIVE WITH IT, TIERA.

CHILDHOOD MEMORIES.

THE GIRL I WAS.

THE WOMAN I BECAME.

HACKER

A HACKER EXTRAORDINAIRE!

ALL POWERFUL, ALL KNOWING.

BUT ALL WASTED KNOWLEDGE ON A PITIFUL SHELL OF A HUMAN.

NOTHING MORE THAN A FRIGGIN' GHOST IN A MACHINE.

I WAS ONE OF THE BEST THERE EVER WAS. A HACKER EXTRAORDINAIRE. CREAM OF THE CROP.

ELITE.

WHAT THE HELL HAPPENED TO ME? WHEN DID I BECOME SUCH A WIMP?

I REMEMBER.

WHEN HE CAME INTO MY LIFE.

OFFERING ME THE TRUTH.

AND I WAS TOO SCARED TO SWALLOW IT.

PATHETIC.

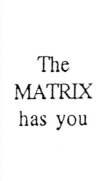

"THE MATRIX", I'D ALMOST FORGOTTEN, AT LEAST WHEN I ALLOW MYSELF TO.

WHAT IS THE MATRIX?

A MAJOR, DAMN, PAIN IN THE ASS QUESTION IS WHAT.

WHY COULDN'T I SEE PAST THE OBVIOUS?

WHY WAS I SO DAMN AFRAID OF THE TRUTH?

I KICK MYSELF IN THE ASS EVERY DAY REMEMBERING HOW MORPHEUS . . .

THE DEALER . . .

THE MASTER HACKER AND KING OF ALL DATA, CAME TO ME AND OFFERED UP A HANDFUL OF ANSWERS AND TRUTHS, AND WHAT DID I DO?

I RAN.

I RAN WITH MY TAIL SHOVED BETWEEN MY TREMBLING LEGS.

LIKE THE PATHETIC SCARED LITTLE DOG I AM.

RED MEANS "GO".
BLUE MEANS "STOP".

I CHOSE BLUE.

DEAD END.
NOWHERE TO
GO BUT DOWN.

NAPOLEON.

JOAN OF ARC.

HITLER.

EINSTEIN.

ALL INSANE, RADICAL
EXTREMISTS.

GOOD OR BAD, THEY ALL
JUMPED OFF HEAD FIRST.
SOME CRASHED AND BURNED,
SOME BECAME GENIUSES.

BUT ALL TRIED IN THE FACE
OF FEAR AND DOUBT.

I DIDN'T.

WHAT WOULD'VE HAPPENED IF I HAD TAKEN THAT LEAP OF FAITH?

WOULD I BE BETTER OFF THAN I AM NOW?

WOULD I BE HAPPIER?

WHAT IS HAPPINESS?

ONE THING FOR DAMN SURE, I KNOW IT'S NOT THIS.

STILL REACHING FOR THAT BRASS RING, WHEN IT'S LONG PAST GRABBING.

I HAD MY CHANCE AND I FRIGGIN' BLEW IT.

IS IT BETTER TO TRY AND FAIL, THAN TO NEVER TRY AT ALL, AND SPEND THE REST OF YOUR LIFE WONDERING WHAT WOULD'VE HAPPENED IF YOU HAD?

I SPEND ALL MY HOURS CALCULATING AND GAUGING THE PEOPLE WHO HAVE TRIED AND SUCCEEDED.

SLEEP
RESTART
SHUTDOWN

EJECT
ERASE DISC

EMPTY TRASH

AND THE LOSERS WHO NEVER TRIED AT ALL.

WHAT WOULD'VE HAPPENED IF I REALLY TRIED?

I'LL NEVER KNOW THE TRUE ANSWER.

AND AS ALWAYS, LIKE THE DAY BEFORE, AND THE DAY YET TO FOLLOW . . .

MY REGRET IS ETERNAL.

END

GOLIATH

STORY NEIL
GAIMAN

Neil Gaiman is likely best known as the creator/writer of the monthly comic series SANDMAN for DC Comics. THE SANDMAN #19 won the 1991 World Fantasy Award for Best Short Story (the first comic ever to receive that literary award). Neil's three part comic series, DEATH: THE HIGH COST OF LIVING was published in February 1993, and DEATH: THE TIME OF YOUR LIFE was released in March 1997, winning the GLAAD award for Best Comic. Outside of comics, Neil has written the English language script for Hayao Miyazaki's PRINCESS MONONOKE, and is now a best selling novelist, penning such titles as STARDUST, AMERICAN GODS (New York Times best seller and winner of the Hugo Award for Best Novel), and CORALINE, which has been optioned for film and is in pre production. Neil returns to the world of comics in 2003 with ENDLESS NIGHTS, a new Sandman anthology, and the series 1602 for Marvel.

ART BY BILL
SIENKIEWICZ
BIO: PAGE 18
VS
GREGORY
RUTH
BIO: PAGE 144

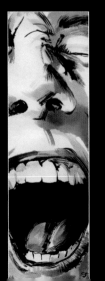

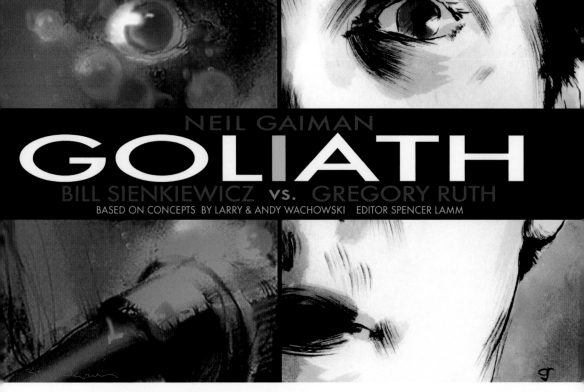

GOLIATH

NEIL GAIMAN

BILL SIENKIEWICZ vs. GREGORY RUTH

BASED ON CONCEPTS BY LARRY & ANDY WACHOWSKI   EDITOR SPENCER LAMM

I suppose that I could claim that I had always suspected that the world was a cheap and shoddy sham, a bad cover for something deeper and weirder and infinitely more strange, and that, in some way, I already knew the truth. But I think that's just how the world has always been. And even now that I know the truth, as you will, my love, if you're reading this, the world still seems cheap and shoddy. Different world, different shoddy, but that's how it feels.

They say, *here's the truth*, and I say, *is that all there is?* And they say, *kind of. Pretty much. As far as we know.*

So. It was 1977, and the nearest I had come to computers was I'd recently bought a big, expensive calculator, and then I'd lost the manual that came with it, so I didn't know what it did any more. I'd add, subtract, multiply and divide, and was grateful I had no need to cos, sine or find tangents or graph functions or whatever else the gizmo did, because, having been turned down by the RAF, I was working as a bookkeeper for a small discount carpet warehouse in Edgware, in North London, near the top of the Northern Line, and I was sitting at the table at the back of the warehouse that served me as a desk when the world began to melt and drip away.

Honest. It was like the walls and the ceiling and the rolls of carpet and the News of the World Topless Calendar were all made of wax, and they started to ooze and run, to flow together and to drip. I could see the houses and the sky and the clouds and the road behind them, and then *that* dripped and flowed away, and behind that was blackness.

I was standing in the puddle of the world, a weird, brightly coloured thing that oozed and brimmed and didn't cover the tops of my brown leather shoes (I have feet like shoeboxes. Boots have to be specially made for me. Costs me a fortune). The puddle cast a weird light upwards.

In fiction, I think I would have refused to believe it was happening, wonder if I'd been drugged or if I was dreaming. In reality, hell, it had happened, and I stared up into the darkness, and then, when nothing happened, I began to walk, splashing through the liquid world, calling out, seeing if anyone was there.

Something flickered in front of me.

"Hey," said a voice. The accent was American, although the intonation was odd.

"Hello," I said.

The flickering continued for a few moments, and then resolved itself into a smartly-dressed man in thick horn-rimmed spectacles.

"You're a pretty big guy," he said. "You know that?"

Of course I knew that. I was 19 years old and I was close to seven feet tall. I have fingers like bananas. I scare children. I'm unlikely to see my 40th birthday: people like me die young.

"What's going on?" I asked. "Do you know?"

"Enemy missile took out a central processing unit," he said. "Two hundred thousand people, hooked up in parallel, blown to dead meat. We've got a mirror going of course, and we'll have it all up and running again in no time flat. You're just free-floating here for a couple of nanoseconds, while we get London processing again."

"Are you God?" I asked. Nothing he had said had made any sense to me.

"Yes. No. Not really," he said. "Not as you mean it, anyway."

And then the world lurched and I found myself coming to work again that morning, poured myself a cup of tea, had the longest, strangest bout of *déjà vu* I've ever had. Twenty minutes, where I knew everything that anyone was going to do or say. And then it went, and time passed properly once more, every second following every other second just like they're meant to.

And the hours passed, and the days, and the years.

I lost my job in the carpet company, and got a new one book-keeping for a company selling business machines, and I got married to a girl called Sandra I met at the swimming baths and we had a couple of kids, both normal sized, and I thought I had the sort of marriage that could survive anything, but I hadn't, so she went away and she took the kiddies with her. I was in my late 20s, and it was 1986, and I got a job on Tottenham Court Road selling computers, and I turned out to be good at it.

I liked computers.

I liked the way they worked. It was an exciting time. I remember our first shipment of ATs, some of them with 40 megabyte hard drives... Well, I was impressed easily back then.

I still lived in Edgware, commuted to work on the Northern Line. I was on the tube one evening, going home – we'd just gone through Euston and half the passengers had got off – looking at the other people in the carriage over the top of the *Evening Standard* and wondering who they were – who they really were, inside – the thin, black girl writing earnestly in her notebook, the little old lady with the green velvet hat on, the girl with the dog, the bearded man with the turban...

And then the tube stopped, in the tunnel.

That was what I thought happened, anyway: I thought the tube had stopped. Everything went very quiet.

And then we went through Euston, and half the passengers got off.

And then we went through Euston, and half the passengers got off. And I was looking at the other passengers and wondering who they really were inside when the train stopped in the tunnel. And everything went very quiet.

And then everything lurched so hard I thought we'd been hit by another train.

And then we went through Euston, and half the passengers got off, and then the train stopped in the tunnel, and then everything went -

(*Normal service will be resumed as soon as possible*, whispered a voice in the back of my head.)

And this time as the train slowed and began to approach Euston I wondered if I was going crazy: I felt like I was jerking back and forth on a video loop. I knew it was happening, but there was nothing I could do to change anything, nothing I could do to break out of it.

The black girl, sitting next to me, passed me a note. ARE WE DEAD? it said.

I shrugged. I didn't know. It seemed as good an explanation as any.

And then everything faded to white.

There was no ground beneath my feet, nothing above me, no sense of distance, no sense of time. I was in a white place. And I was not alone.

The man wore thick horn-rimmed spectacles, and a suit that looked like it might have been Armani. "You again?" he said. "The big guy. I just spoke to you."

"I don't think so," I said.

"Half an hour ago. When the missiles hit."

"Back in the carpet factory? That was years ago."

"About thirty-seven minutes back. We've been running in an accelerated mode since then, trying to patch and cover, while we've been processing potential solutions."

"Who sent the missiles?" I asked. "The U.S.S.R.? The Iranians?"

"Aliens," he said.

"You're kidding?"

"Not as far as we can tell. We've been sending out seed-probes for a couple of hundred years now. Looks like something has followed one back. We learned about it when the first missiles landed. It's taken us a good twenty minutes to get a retaliatory plan up and running. That's why we've been processing in overdrive. Did it seem like the last decade went pretty fast?"

"Yeah. I suppose."

"That's why. We ran it through pretty fast, trying to maintain a common reality while processing."

"So what are you going to do?"

"We're going to counter-attack. We're going to take them out. It's going to take a while: we don't have the machinery right now. We have to build it."

The white was fading into dark pinks and dull reds. I opened my eyes. For the first time.

So. Sharp the world and tangled-tubed and strange and dark and somewhere beyond belief. It made no sense. Nothing made sense. It was real, and it was a nightmare. It lasted for thirty seconds, and each cold second felt like a tiny forever.

And then we went through Euston, and half the passengers got off...

I started talking to the black girl with the notebook. Her name was Susan. Several weeks later she moved in with me.

Time rumbled and rolled. I suppose I was becoming sensitive to it. Maybe I knew what I was looking for – knew there was something to look for, even if I didn't know what it was.

I made the mistake of telling Susan some of what I believed one night – about how none of this was real. About how we were really just hanging there, plugged and wired, central processing units or just cheap memory chips for some computer the size of the world, being fed a consensual hallucination to keep us happy, to allow us to communicate and dream using the tiny fraction of our brains that they weren't using to crunch numbers and store information.

"We're memory," I told her. "That's what we are. Memory."

"You don't really believe this stuff," she told me, and her voice was trembling. "It's a story."

When we made love, she always wanted me to be rough with her, but I never dared. I didn't know my own strength, and I'm so clumsy. I didn't want to hurt her. I never wanted to hurt her, so I stopped telling her my ideas.

It didn't matter. She moved out the following weekend.

I missed her.

The moments of déjà vu were coming more frequently, now. Moments would stutter and hiccup and falter and repeat.

And then I woke up one morning and it was 1975 again, and I was sixteen, and after a day of hell at school I was walking out of school, into the RAF recruiting office next to the kebab house in Chapel Road.

"You're a big lad," said the recruiting officer. I thought he was American, but he said he was Canadian. He wore big horn-rimmed glasses.

"Yes," I said.

"And you want to fly?"

"More than anything," I said. It seemed like I half-remembered a world in which I'd forgotten that I wanted to fly planes, which seemed as strange to me as forgetting my own name.

"Well," said the horn-rimmed man, "We're going to have to bend a few rules. But we'll have you up in the air in no time." And he meant it, too.

The next few years passed really fast. It seemed like I spent all of them in planes of different kinds, cramped into tiny cockpits, in seats I barely fitted, flicking switches too small for my fingers.

I got Secret clearance, then I got Noble clearance, which leaves Secret clearance in the shade, and then I got Graceful clearance, which the Prime Minister himself doesn't have, by which time I was piloting flying saucers and other craft that moved with no visible means of support.

I started dating a girl called Sandra, and then we got married, because if we married we got to move into married quarters, which was a nice little semidetached house near Dartmoor. We never had any children: I had been warned that it was possible I might have been exposed to enough radiation to fry my gonads, and it seemed sensible not to try for kids, under the circumstances: didn't want to breed monsters.

It was 1985 when the man with horn-rimmed spectacles walked into my house.

My wife was at her mother's that week. Things had got a bit tense, and she'd moved out to buy herself some 'breathing room'. She said I was getting on her nerves. But if I was getting on anyone's nerves, I think it must have been my own. It seemed like I knew what was going to happen all the time. Not just me: it seemed like everyone knew what was going to happen. Like we were sleepwalking through our lives for the tenth or the twentieth or the hundredth time.

I wanted to tell Sandra, but somehow I knew better, knew I'd lose her if I opened my mouth. Still, I seemed to be losing her anyway. So I was sitting in the lounge watching *The Tube* on Channel Four and drinking a mug of tea, and feeling sorry for myself.

The man with the horn-rimmed specs walked into my house like he owned the place. He checked his watch.

"Right," he said. "Time to go. You'll be piloting something pretty close to a PL-47."

Even people with Graceful clearance weren't meant to know about PL-47s. I'd flown one a dozen times. Looked like a tea-cup, flew like something from *Star Wars*.

"Shouldn't I leave a note for Sandra?" I asked.

"No," he said, flatly. "Now, sit down on the floor and breathe deeply, and regularly. In, out, in out."

It never occurred to me to argue with him, or to disobey. I sat down on the floor, and I began to breathe, slowly, in and out and out and in and...

In.

Out.

In.

A wrenching. The worst pain I've ever felt. I was choking.

In.

Out.

I was screaming, but I could hear my voice and I wasn't screaming. All I could hear was a low bubbling moan.

In.

Out.

It was like being born. It wasn't comfortable, or pleasant. It was the breathing carried me through it, through all the pain and the darkness and the bubbling in my lungs. I opened my eyes.

I was lying on a metal disk about eight feet across. I was naked, wet and surrounded by a sprawl of cables. They were retracting, moving away from me, like scared worms or nervous brightly coloured snakes.

I was naked. I looked down at my body. No body hair, no wrinkles. I wondered how old I was, in real terms. Eighteen? Twenty? I couldn't tell.

There was a glass screen set into the floor of the metal disk. It flickered and came to life. I was staring at the man in the horn-rimmed spectacles.

"Do you remember?" he asked. "You should be able to access most of your memory for the moment."

"I think so," I told him.

"You'll be in a PL-47," he said. "We've just finished building it. Pretty much had to go back to first principles, come forward. Modify some factories to construct it. We'll have another batch of them finished by tomorrow. Right now we've only got one."

"So if this doesn't work, you've got replacements for me."

"If we survive that long," he said. "Another missile bombardment started about fifteen minutes ago. Took out most of Australia. We project that it's still a prelude to the real bombing."

"What are they dropping? Nuclear weapons?"

"Rocks."

"Rocks?"

"Uh-huh. Rocks. Asteroids. Big ones. We think that tomorrow unless we surrender, they may drop the moon on us."

"You're joking."

"Wish I was." The screen went dull.

The metal disk had been navigating its way through a tangle of cables and a world of sleeping naked people. It had slipped over sharp microchip towers and softly glowing silicone spires.

The PL-47 was waiting for me at the top of a metal mountain. Tiny metal crabs scuttled across it, polishing and checking every last rivet and stud.

I walked inside on tree-trunk legs that still trembled and shook. I sat down in the pilot's chair, and was thrilled to realise that it had been built for me. It fitted. I strapped myself down. My hands began to go through warm-up sequence. Cables crept over my arms. I felt something plugging into the base of my spine, something else moving in and connecting at the top of my neck.

My perception of the ship expanded radically. I had it in 360 degrees, above, below. And at the same time, I was sitting in the cabin, activating the launch codes.

"Good luck," said the horn-rimmed man on a tiny screen to my left.

"Thank you. Can I ask one last question?"

"I don't see why not."

"Why me?"

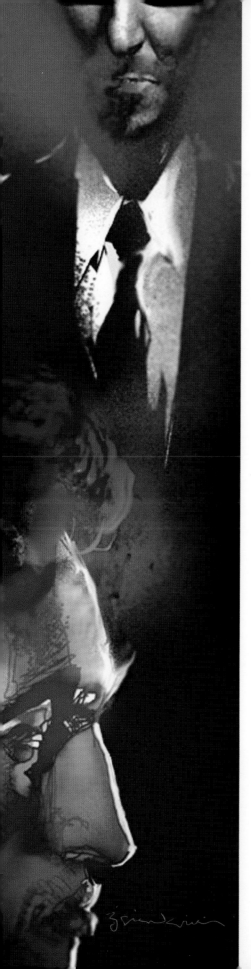

"Well," he said, "the short answer is that you were designed to do this. We've improved a little on the basic human design in your case. You're bigger. You're much faster. You have faster processing speeds and reaction times."

"I'm not faster. I'm big, but I'm clumsy."

"Not in real life," he said. "That's just in the world."

And I took off.

I never saw the aliens, if there were any aliens, but I saw their ship. It looked like fungus or seaweed: the whole thing was organic, an enormous glimmering thing, orbiting the moon. It looked like something you'd see growing on a rotting log, half-submerged under the sea. It was the size of Tasmania.

Two-hundred mile-long sticky tendrils were dragging asteroids of various sizes behind them. It reminded me a little of the trailing tendrils of a portuguese man o' war, that strange compound sea-creature.

They started throwing rocks at me as I got a couple of hundred thousand miles away.

My fingers were activating the missile bay, aiming at a floating nucleus, while I wondered what I was doing. I wasn't saving the world I knew. That world was imaginary: a sequence of ones and zeroes. I was saving a nightmare...

But if the nightmare died, the dream was dead too.

There was a girl named Susan. I remembered her, from a ghost-life long gone. I wondered if she was still alive (had it been a couple of hours? Or a couple of lifetimes?). I supposed she was dangling from cables somewhere, with no memory of a miserable, paranoid giant.

I was so close I could see the ripples of the thing. The rocks were getting smaller, and more accurate. I dodged and wove and skimmed. Part of me was just admiring the economy of the thing: no expensive explosives to build and buy. Just good old kinetic energy.

If one of those things had hit the ship I would have been dead. Simple as that.

The only way to avoid them was to outrun them. So I kept running.

The nucleus was staring at me. It was an eye of some kind. I was certain of it.

I was a hundred yards away from the nucleus when I let the payload go. Then I ran.

I wasn't quite out of range when the thing imploded. It was like fireworks – beautiful in a ghastly sort of way. And then there was nothing but a faint trace of glitter and dust...

"I did it!" I screamed. "I did it! I ----ing well did it!"

The screen flickered. Horn-rimmed spectacles were staring at me. There was no real face behind them any more. Just a loose approximation of concern and interest. "You did it," he agreed.

"Now, where do I bring this thing down?" I asked.

There was a hesitation, then, "You don't. We didn't design it to return. It was a redundancy we had no need for. Too costly, in terms of resources."

"So what do I do? I just saved the Earth. And now I suffocate out here?"

He nodded. "That's pretty much it. Yes."

The lights began to dim. One by one, the controls were going out. I lost my 360 degree perception of the ship. It was just me, strapped to a chair in the middle of nowhere, inside a flying teacup.

"How long do I have?"

"We're closing down all your systems, but you've got a couple of hours, at least. We're not going to evacuate the remaining air. That would be inhuman."

"You know, in the world I came from, they would have given me a medal."

"Obviously, we're grateful."

"So you can't come up with any more tangible way to express your gratitude?"

"Not really. You're a disposable part. A unit. We can't mourn

047

you any more than a wasps' nest mourns the death of a single wasp. It's not sensible and it's not viable to bring you back."

"And you don't want this kind of firepower coming back toward the Earth, where it could be used against you?"

"As you say."

And then the screen went dark, with not so much as a goodbye. *Do not adjust your set*, I thought. *Reality is at fault.*

You become very aware of your breathing, when you only have a couple of hours of air. In. Hold. Out. Hold. In. Hold. Out. Hold....

I sat there strapped to my seat in the half-dark, and I waited, and I thought. Then I said, "Hello? Is anybody there?"

A beat. The screen flickered with patterns. "Yes?"

"I have a request. Listen. You – you people, machines, whatever you are – you owe me one. Right? I mean I saved all your lives."

"...Continue."

"I've got a couple of hours left. Yes?"

"About 57 minutes."

"Can you plug me back into the... the real world. The other world. The one I came from?"

"Mm? I don't know. I'll see." Dark screen once more.

I sat and breathed, in and out, in and out, while I waited. I felt very peaceful. If it wasn't for having less than an hour to live, I'd have felt just great.

The screen glowed. There was no picture, no pattern, no nothing. Just a gentle glow. And a voice, half in my head, half out of it, said, "You got a deal."

There was a sharp pain at the base of my skull. Then blackness, for several minutes.

Then this.

That was fifteen years ago: 1984. I went back into computers. I own my computer store on the Tottenham Court Road. And now, as we head toward the new millennium, I'm writing this down. This time around, I married Susan. It took me a couple of months to find her. We have a son.

I'm nearly forty. People of my kind don't live much longer than that, on the whole. Our hearts stop. When you read this, I'll be dead. You'll know that I'm dead. You'll have seen a coffin big enough for two men dropped into a hole.

But know this, Susan, my sweet: my true coffin is orbiting the moon. It looks like a flying teacup. They gave me the world back, and you back, for a little while. Last time I told you, or someone like you, the truth, or what I knew of it, you walked out on me. And maybe that wasn't you, and I wasn't me, but I don't dare risk it again. So I'm going to write this down, and you'll be given it with the rest of my papers when I'm gone. Goodbye.

They may be heartless, unfeeling, computerised bastards, leeching off the minds of what's left of humanity. But I can't help feeling grateful to them.

I'll die soon. But the last twenty minutes have been the best years of my life.

BURNING HOPE

STORY & ART BY JOHN
VAN FLEET

John Van Fleet's first award came on June 1st, 1984, when he was handed a Bachelor of Arts in Communication from the Pratt Institute School of Arts and Design. He has been an active artist in the comic industry since 1982, when he did the contents page art for DARKSTORM ILLUSTRATED ADVENTURE series #1. In the following years he has done interior art and covers for numerous comics, including: TYPHOID (1995), written by Ann Nocenti, BATMAN: THE CHALICE (1999) and BATMAN: THE ANKH (2001), both written by Chuck Dixon. You can also see John's work in mag-azines, on magazine covers, on posters, cards, and on book covers such as CLAN NOVEL: GANGREL, and collected in the art book THE ART OF JOHN VAN FLEET.

BURNING H⊕PE
Story and Art by John Van Fleet

Edited by Spencer Lamm

From concepts by
Larry and Andy Wachowski

I'M HERE... I THINK.
THIS PLACE IS A
REAL HOLE.

IT'S AN ORPHANAGE
EIGHT BALL, WHAT WERE
YOU EXPECTING, MONKEY
BARS AN' MURALS?

YEAH WELL, YOU WOULD
THINK THE CHURCH COULD
DO BETTER THAN THIS DUMP.
AND BY THE WAY, I'M NOT
TOO JAZZED ABOUT
LYING TO A NUN.

LOOK AROUND YOU
EIGHT BALL... WHO'S
BEEN LYING TO WHO?

RIGHT... LAND OF THE FREE,
HOME OF THE SLAVE.

AMEN.

HOUSTON, WE MAY
HAVE A PROBLEM.

DO YOU SEE
THE GIRL?
IS SHE OK?

CHARON, I'M TOUCHED
BY YOUR CONCERN.

DON'T BE AN ASS
EIGHT BALL, YOU
KNOW WHAT THE
ORACLE SAID.

WELL I BET THE
ORACLE DIDN'T
SEE THIS COMING!

THIS PLACE IS TOAST!
YOU MUST BE READ-ING YESTERDAY'S CODE CHARON, WE'RE TALKING A 4-ALARM BAKE SALE.
ANY... BODIES?
NO, CHALK PEOPLE. I GUESS EVERYONE GOT OUT IN TIME.
A BIT IRONIC DON'T YOU THINK? I MEAN, IT WAS SAINT GEORGE THAT KILLED THE DRAGON, WASN'T IT?
YOU'VE BEEN HOLDING OUT ON ME, DO YOU HAVE A CHECKERED SKIRT IN YOUR PAST?
GET SERIOUS EIGHT BALL, I CAN'T FIND ANYTHING ON-LINE ABOUT ANY FIRE AT THAT LOCATION.
THE POLICE NEVER GOT A CALL... THE FIRE DEPARTMENT SHOWS NOTHING FOR THAT ADDRESS, AND THE PAPERS WOULD NEVER MISS THIS KIND OF STORY!

YOU DID ALL YOU COULD. YOU CAN'T GO ON BLAMING...

MYSELF? NEWS FLASH DUNCAN, EIGHT BALL WAS SET UP. THEY KNEW WHERE AND THEY KNEW WHEN.

I'M DOING MY JOB... WHO'S DOING YOURS?

MY FAULT, SORRY... I WAS JUST TRYING TO... I MEAN I HAD NO IDEA THAT AGENTS...

I BELIEVE SHE'S ALREADY MADE THAT POINT DUNCAN, SO LET'S MOVE ON TO THE QUESTION OF, WHAT NOW?

YOU LOST ME!

I'M SHOCKED. WE NEED AN IDEA OF WHAT THE HELL WE'RE UP AGAINST.

I SAY WE SIT TIGHT. THE CAPTAIN WILL BE BACK FROM ZION TOMORROW AND WE CAN FIGURE THIS WHOLE MESS OUT THEN.

AND TO PASS THE TIME WE CAN HAVE THE SMITHS OVER FOR TEA.

SHE HAS A POINT. AS LONG AS THAT TAG PROGRAM IS ACTIVE WE'RE SQUID BAIT.

GET ME A FIX!

IT'S SOMETHING THE ORACLE SAID - 'AND THE CHILD WOULD BE HOPE'. WE THOUGHT THIS WAS ABOUT SAVING OURSELVES... BUT THAT'S HER NAME-- HOPE. SHE HAS THE TAG, CHARON.

THAT'S GREAT LINK, AND I SWEAR I WOULD BE ALL WARM AND FUZZY IF YOU WERE STANDING HERE, AND NOT AT *GROUND ZERO!*

IF THIS WERE A TRAP, I'D BE DEAD. THEY WEREN'T AFTER EIGHT BALL, THEY WERE AFTER HOPE.

THEN SHE'S ALREADY DEAD.

I DON'T THINK SO... GET ME A FIX ON THE TAG.

IT'S WEAK, BUT YOU'RE CLOSE. LINK, THINK ABOUT IT, SHE'S PART OF THE MATRIX, SHE CAN'T HIDE.

THEY ARE EVERY- WHERE, THEY ARE EVERY- ONE. THE GIRL IS...

SHE'S ALIVE, CHARON, AND SHE KNOWS ABOUT THE MATRIX.

LET'S SAY YOU'RE RIGHT, LET'S SAY SHE IS AWARE, GIFTED, WHATEVER, THE ORACLE KNEW, AND WE DREW THE SHORT STRAW.

IT DOESN'T ADD UP, SHE COULDN'T OUT-RUN THEM-- SHE'S JUST A KID.

I'VE GOT COMPANY.

IS IT HER? I HAVE THE TAG, STRONG! STRAIGHT AHEAD.

HELLO... SIR... CAN YOU HELP ME? PLEASE, I WON'T HURT YOU, I'M JUST LOOKING FOR THE LITTLE GIRL... HOPE.

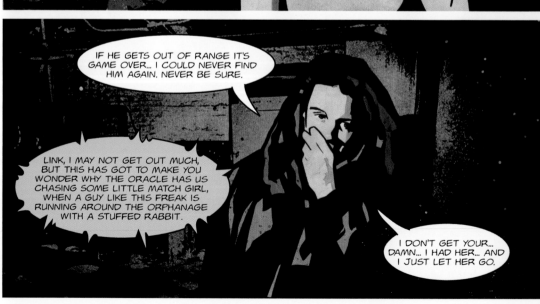

061

BUTTERFLY

STORY & ART BY DAVE
GIBBONS

Comic industry veteran Dave Gibbons has been involved in the comic world for the last 25 years. While residing in his native UK, his work has been published throughout the Americas, Europe and Japan. Dave was a co-creator of ROGUE TROOPER for 2000AD, as well as the MARTHA WASHINGTON series with Frank Miller. Probably his most popular work is the award winning comic series, WATCHMEN. His oeuvre can also be seen in issues of BATMAN, SUPERMAN and DR. WHO, among others. In addition to collaborating with Stan Lee on a reinterpretation of the character Green Lantern, Dave's latest work includes the forthcoming DC Comics/Vertigo graphic novel THE ORIGINALS.

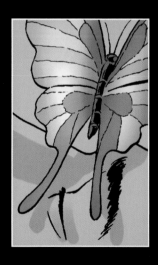

BUTTERFLY by Dave Gibbons

Based on concepts by Larry & Andy Wachowski

Chuang Tzu had a dream

In the dream he was a butterfly

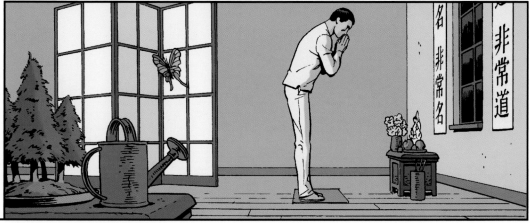

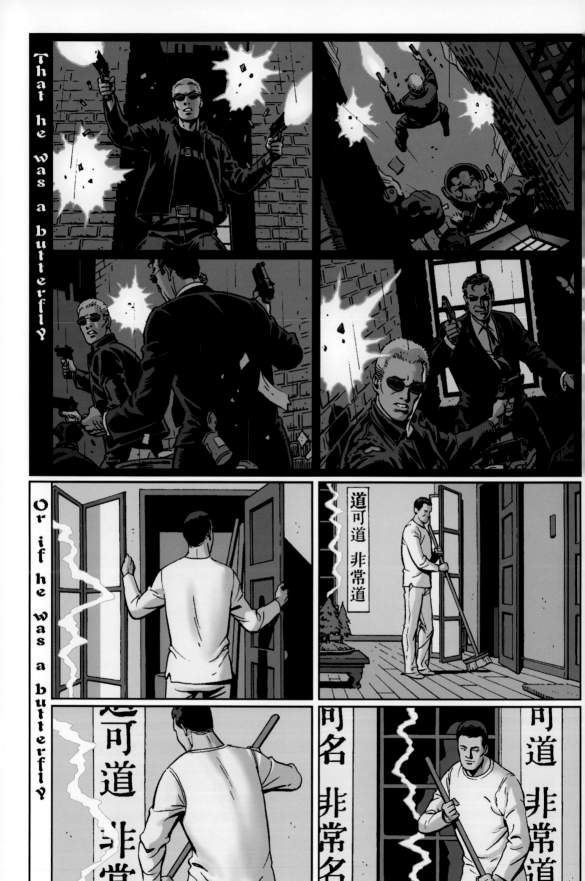

BRRIINNNG

BRRIINNNG

BRRIINNNG

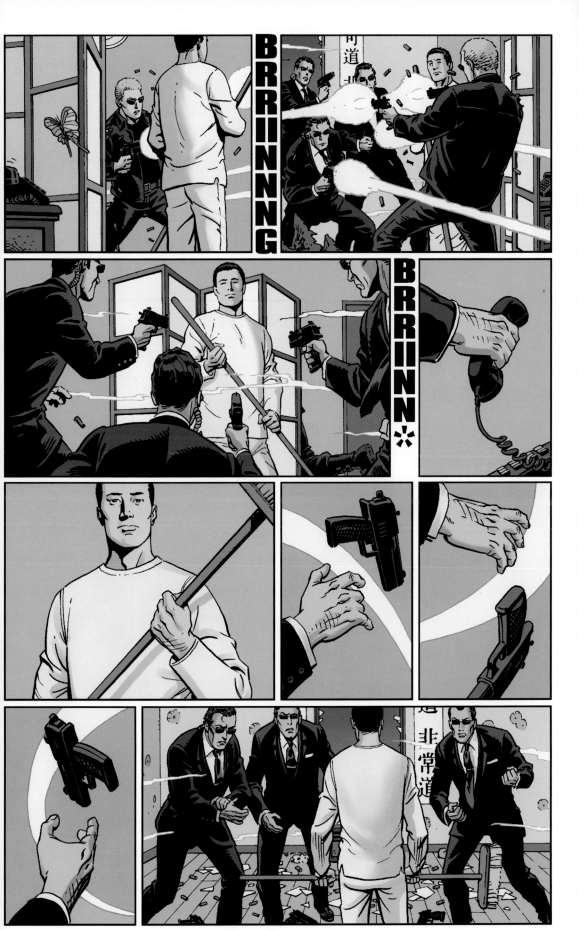

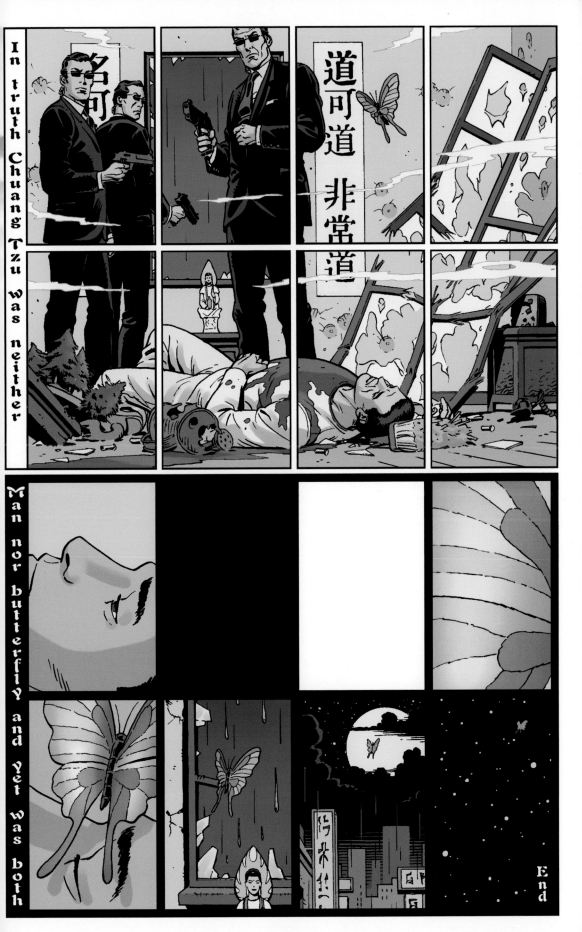

In truth Chuang Tzu was neither

道可道 非常道

名可

Man nor butterfly and yet was both

End

A SWORD OF A DIFFERENT COLOR

STORY & ART BY TROY
NIXEY

Troy Nixey has illustrated a number of notable creators' work. They include Mike Mignola who wrote: BATMAN: THE DOOM THAT CAME TO GOTHAM and BATMAN: THE GASWORKS, Neil Gaiman who wrote (with P. Craig Russell adapting): IT'S ONLY THE END OF THE WORLD AGAIN, and Matt Wagner who wrote GRENDEL: BLACK, WHITE & RED. Troy co-created the comic mini series JENNY FINN with Mike Mignola; he created the BACON comic as well as the critically acclaimed comic, TROUT. His favorite project to date was a story he wrote and drew in BART SIMPSON'S TREEHOUSE OF HORROR #7. Future projects include a chapter in X-MEN UNLIMITED #37: SACRIFICIAL WORLDS, written by Kaare Andrews… and there will, of course, be more TROUT!

COLOR BY DAVE
McCAIG

Dave McCaig is perhaps best known for his coloring work on Dark Horse Comics' Buffy the Vampire Slayer and Angel titles, where he uses his unique palette and style to bring their adventures to life every month. With work on Marvel Comics' X-Men titles as well as the color work on the official adaptation of Star Wars: Attack of the Clones under his belt, McCaig is also a distinguished painter in his own right, having illustrated many Star Wars covers for Dark Horse.

A SWORD OF A DIFFERENT COLOR

TROY NIXEY
WORDS & PICTURES

DAVE McCAIG
PAINTING

SPENCER LAMM
EDITOR

BASED ON CONCEPTS BY
LARRY & ANDY WACHOWSKI

NACS' QUARTERS

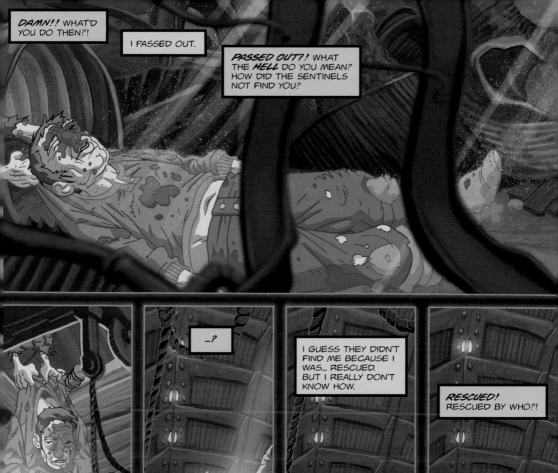

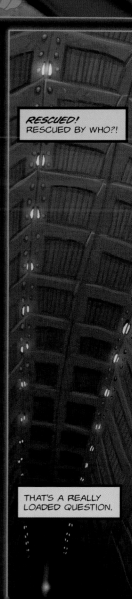

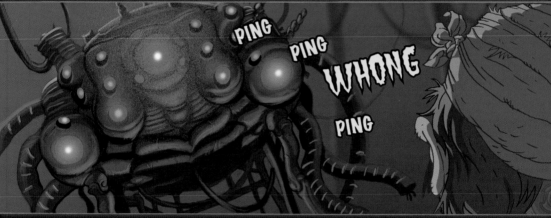

...!

THIS GUY IS *CRAZY!*

AS A LOON.

THEN THINGS GOT WORSE. A FEVER SET IN AND THE CRAZY OLD COOT ACTUALLY DID A PRETTY GOOD JOB OF KEEPING ME ALIVE. HE HAD JERRY RIGGED SOME DEVICE THAT TRAPPED CONDENSATION, AND WAS AT LEAST SMART ENOUGH TO BOIL THE WATER FIRST BEFORE WE DRANK IT.

I CAN'T SAY MUCH ABOUT THE MENU THOUGH... I ATE WHAT I THINK WAS SOME KIND OF COCKROACH PASTE...

I'M NOT *EVEN* GONNA TELL YOU WHAT HE ATE!

EEEHHH...

...AND OF COURSE, THERE WAS ALWAYS THE TALKING.

AS A KNIGHT OF THE HIGHEST ORDER, IT IS MY SWORN DUTY TO VANQUISH THESE FOUL DRAGONS.

VERILY THEY HAVE SUNK THEIR EVIL CLAWS DEEP INTO THE HEART OF US ALL. BUT I WILL REND FREE FROM THEIR VILE GRIP, AND BREATHE AS A FREE MAN SHOULD.

FREEDOM, FREEDOM I SAY!

IT WAS ABOUT THIS TIME DURING HIS SPEECHES THAT MY MIND WOULD START TO WANDER.

I REALIZED THIS MAN HAD NO COMPREHENSION AS TO HIS ORIGINS, NO UNDERSTANDING OF THE REAL WORLD...

HE LIVED IN HIS OWN WORLD... MAYBE HE WAS BETTER OFF FOR IT.

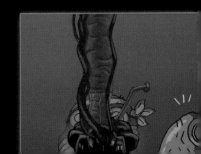

YOU KNOW THAT FEELING YOU GET WHEN YOU'VE SEEN SOMETHING BEFORE, BUT YOU CAN'T QUITE PUT YOUR FINGER ON IT? THAT'S HOW HIS DRAWINGS MADE ME FEEL.

HIS VILE DRAGONS, THE ONES HE TALKED ENDLESSLY ABOUT, THE ONES HE VOWED TO DEFEAT... THEY WERE THE *FETUS HARVESTERS!*

090

IT WENT ON LIKE THAT FOR A WHILE, TILL FINALLY ONE MORNING...

ZZZ... SNORT

...YAWN

IF WAS THE FIRST FULL NIGHT OF SLEEP I'D HAD IN SOME TIME. I MUST HAVE BEEN EXHAUSTED, BECAUSE I NEVER HEARD HIM LEAVE... AND HE HAD TAKEN THE SENTINEL WITH HIM.

HE DID LEAVE A LITTLE PACKAGE FOR ME THOUGH.

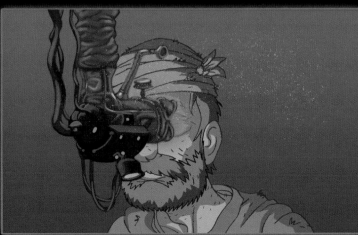

IT ALL BECAME VERY CLEAR THEN WHAT HIS PLAN WAS.

WHAT? WHAT'D HE DO?!

I'M GETTING TO THAT. HE WASN'T VERY HARD TO SPOT.

HE HAD ATTRACTED MORE THAN HIS FAIR SHARE OF SENTINELS.

AND THEN WHAT HAPPENED?!

1.23

1.52

WAHBOOM!!

HE KICKED THE MACHINES *RIGHT IN THE BALLS.*

I CAN'T EVEN BEGIN TO TELL YOU HOW MUCH DESTRUCTION HE CAUSED WITH THAT EXPLOSION.

THAT WAS HIM? I HEARD ONE OF THE FIELDS TOOK A GOOD HIT, BUT I THOUGHT THAT WASJUST A RUMOR. THAT WAS HIM? SHEESH!

1.52

.63

AFTER THAT I DID SOME SNOOPIN' AROUND - HE HAD STORES OF SUPPLIES SQUIRRELED AWAY - INCLUDING A CRATE THAT HELD *CYCLONITE*, BUT WAS EMPTY. I FIGURE ALL THE CRAP HE WELDED TO THE SENTINEL WAS SHRAPNEL... HE DEFINITELY HAD SOME KIND OF PLAN, THAT'S FOR SURE.

WOW! WHO'D HAVE THOUGHT SOME CRAZY OLD COOT COULD PULL OFF SOMETHING LIKE THAT!

OH MAN, THAT'S A STORY TO TELL YOUR GRANDKIDS' GRANDKIDS. YOU GET SOME REST NOW, I'LL BE BY TOMORROW TO CHECK ON YA.

YEAH, I AM PRETTY TIRED. OH... AND IT'S REALLY GOOD TO SEE YOU AGAIN.

YOU TOO BUDDY, YOU TOO.

CRAZY?

...

FFFPPPTTT... CRAZY MY ASS!

GET IT?

STORY & ART BY PETER
BAGGE

Peter Bagge's debut comic strip was seen in The East Village Eye in 1980, and he continued to be published regularly in other periodicals, such as High Times and Screw. In 1985 Peter's first self written and illustrated title came into being: NEAT STUFF. That was followed in 1990 with HATE, a semi-autobiographical comic series set in Seattle, written and illustrated by Peter. A voracious artist, Peter has completed comic strips and other works of art including, DONNA'S DAY: MISSIVE DEVICE, a 16 page color mini comic, and gag panels which appear in KUTIE. Other works can be found in YEAH!, DETAILS, and the one-shot look at Marvel's favorite web-slinger, STARTLING STORIES: THE MEGALOMANIACAL SPIDER-MAN. In addition to more HATE, be sure to check out Peter's monthly comic SWEATSHOP from DC Comics.

097

END!

THERE ARE NO FLOWERS
IN THE REAL WORLD

STORY & ART BY DAVID
LAPHAM

Writer and artist David Lapham began work at 17 as a layout artist for the Ocean County Observer. He began his career in the comic industry at 20, illustrating and helping create many original titles at Valiant Comics, including SHADOWMAN and HARBINGER. The independent publishing company, EL CAPITAN BOOKS, was co-founded in 1995 by David and Maria Lapham, under which they began publishing David's comic series, STRAY BULLETS. David won an Eisner award in 1996 for Best Writer / Artist; he has been nominated five times in that category. David is also the creator of the comic novel, MURDER ME DEAD.

Edited by Spencer Lamm   Based on concepts by Larry & Andy Wachowski

...oh, no...

ungh... ahh...

BEEP BEEP

WE'RE SORRY. NO ONE IS AVAILABLE TO TAKE YOUR CALL. PLEASE LEAVE A MESSAGE AT THE TONE....

God...

BEEEEP!

THIS IS ROCKET.... I'M WITH THE MARINER. OUR SHIP WAS ATTA-- ATTACKED. EVERYONE IS DEAD! I'M TRAPPED. I'M TRAPPED IN THE MATRIX!

CLICK!.... SLOW DOWN. STAY CALM. I SEE YOU.... YOU NEED TO MOVE. NOW! PEOPLE ARE COMING.

YOU'RE NEXT TO A RESTAURANT.

YES.

GO AROUND BEHIND THE BUILDING. GO INSIDE. SIT DOWN CALMLY AND ORDER A CUP OF COFFEE. THEN CALL BACK.

I CAN'T MOVE...

...I'M HAVING A PROBLEM WITH MY LEG.

SPAK

SPAK

I THINK IT MAY REALLY BE BROKEN!

YOUR LEG MAY REALLY BE BROKEN, BUT THAT IS NOT REALLY YOUR LEG....

FEEL BETTER?

JUST PARANOID. I'M A SITTING DUCK IF ANY OF THESE PEOPLE TURN INTO AGENTS.

IF AGENTS WERE LOOKING FOR YOU, YOU'D ALREADY BE DEAD.... TELL ME WHAT HAPPENED.

THE FOUR OF US WERE HEADED FOR PHOENIX. WE WERE ABOUT TWENTY MINUTES OUT...

...WHEN WE GOT A CALL FROM ROOK, OUR OPERATOR.

IT WASN'T VERY CLEAR, BUT THE MARINER WAS UNDER ATTACK. SENTINELS, I GUESS.

SPEEDY PULLED OFF THE ROAD AND HEADED FOR THE NEAREST EXIT...

...BUT HE SUDDENLY GRABBED HIS CHEST AND SLUMPED OVER.

NEARLY FLIPPED THE CAR.

THEN THEY ALL STARTED GOING DOWN....

BRRRING!

DEUCE... SHE...

BRRRING!

103

I HEARD AN EXPLOSION, AND THE LINE WENT DEAD. I'M STILL ALIVE, SO ROOK MUST HAVE NAILED THEM... BUT I GUESS HE BOUGHT IT, TOO...

GOD BLESS THIS COUNTRY HOME

SOMETHING HAPPENED TO THE EXIT?

I...uh...I LOST MY TEMPER.

?

DO YOU KNOW WHERE YOU ARE?

YEAH, uh... OUTSIDE PHOENIX--

--IN GOODYEAR. IN A CRACKER BARREL. TWO HUNDRED YARDS FROM THE INTERSTATE. **NO.** WHERE ARE **YOU?** WHERE IS THE MARINER?

gulp gulp

ENJOY

OH!...Oh, God... IT'S MY FIRST MISSION. I... TOKYO... I REMEMBER ROOK SAID SOMETHING ABOUT **TOKYO.**

GOOD. THE PEQUOD IS ON ITS WAY TO FIND YOU. I'M GOING TO GIVE YOU THE ADDRESS OF A SAFE HOUSE. IT'S EAST OF PHOENIX IN THE TOWN OF SCOTTSDALE....

I KNOW WHERE THAT IS. IT'S WHERE I'M FROM....

FOUR DAYS LATER...

SPAK!

SPAK!

HOW ARE WE FEELING THIS MORNING?

L-LEG b-broke again last n-night. It's-- it's getting... hard, king. T-too hard... I d-don't think... they're going t-to f-find, me in time.... I c-can't last m-much l-longer...

YOU'RE THINKING ABOUT IT TOO MUCH. GET YOUR MIND ON SOMETHING ELSE.

WHAT DID YOU DO BEFORE?

I...WASN'T WHAT Y-YOU'D C-C-CALL A MODEL CITIZEN.

WHO WAS? I ENGINEERED WHAT, AT THE TIME, WAS THE LARGEST STOCK SCAM IN THE HISTORY OF WALL STREET.

104

AND THAT WAS BACK **BEFORE** THE INTERNET DAYS.

I KNOCKED OVER ATM'S. I WAS PRETTY MUCH A STREET KID.... I HUNG WITH THIS DIRTBAG NAMED LARRY LITTLE. I THOUGHT HE WAS **GREAT**. HE AND HIS GOONS WERE INTO ALL KINDS OF STUFF.... I WAS GOOD WITH COMPUTERS, SO THEY PUT ME TO WORK BUSTIN' CASH MACHINES.

REAL VISIONARIES. DID YOU HAVE A GIRL?

HER NAME WAS MONA.

SHE WAS A SWEET THING, I'LL BET....YOU WERE IN LOVE?

NO...IT'S ALL FAKE, ANYWAY. JUST PART OF THIS STUPID **COMPUTER** PROGRAM.

HEY, MAN, LOVE IS LOVE. IT'S IN THE **SOUL**.....IT DOESN'T CARE IF YOUR BODY'S MADE OF FLESH AND BLOOD OR ZEROES AND ONES.

ANYWAY, SHE'S THE ENEMY. SHE'S PART OF THE **MATRIX**.

WELL...

...I'LL TELL YA, WE DO OUR JOBS RIGHT, AND SOMEDAY WE'LL SAVE **ALL** THE PRETTY GIRLS.

LATE THAT NIGHT...

PING!

KLAK KLAK KLAK

LARRY?

MONA...

IT'S ME, MONA...

...COME RIDE WITH ME.

ROCKET?!

COME RIDE WITH ME.

LORD, ROCKET, MY PARENTS'LL KILL ME.

RRRRRRRRRRRRR

105

I'M--I'M IN **SHOCK**. I THOUGHT YOU WERE **DEAD**. AND THEN YOU JUST... **SHOW UP**! WHA-- WHAT HAPPENED?

GOD, YOU'RE BEAUTIFUL.

SERIOUSLY, ROCKET, WHERE HAVE YOU BEEN?

I CAN'T BELIEVE HOW GOOD YOU MAKE ME FEEL.

YOU'RE NOT GOING TO ANSWER ME, ARE YOU?

AFTER, YOU WANT TO GO DOWN TO DENNY'S? **LARRY** AND THE GUYS'D **LOVE** TO SEE YOU.

NO!... I...um... I JUST WANT TO BE WITH **YOU**.

ROCKET...

...ARE YOU TRYING TO TELL ME SOMETHING?

BOY, I'M THIRSTY.... I'LL BE RIGHT BACK.

YEAH...

YOU'RE ALL SUCKERS!

SLAVES! SLAVES TO THE MACHINES!

YOU'RE SWIMMING IN VATS OF GLOP WITH GIANT **TUBES** SHOVED UP YOUR BUTTS!

THERE ARE NO **FLOWERS** IN THE REAL WORLD!

YOU THINK YOU'RE HURTIN, LARRY OL' BOY?... **I'M** HURT! **REALLY** HURT!... *MY LEG--* IF YOU KNEW...

GET UP, BOY-O IT'S ALL IN YOUR **MIND!**

HEAL THYSELF!

THE NEXT DAY...

DING-DONG!

YES?-- OH!

MS. THOMAS? I'M **AGENT BROWN.**... I'M... LOOKING FOR A YOUNG MAN.... HIS NAME IS HAROLD ZINSSER, BUT HE OFTEN GOES BY THE NAME OF... **ROCKET.**

YEAH. I-I KNOW HIM, BUT I HAVEN'T SEEN HIM IN A **LONG** TIME. **MONTHS**... JERK LEFT ME.

IS THAT SO?... WELL, MS. THOMAS, I WOULD APPRECIATE IT IF YOU WOULD... CALL ME IF YOU **HEAR** FROM THIS MAN. HE IS **EXTREMELY**... DANGEROUS.

AGENT BROWN

LAST NIGHT, HE **KILLED** A MAN.

OH... YEAH. SURE.

ELSEWHERE...

g-good news...m-my leg s-s-stopped bleeding.... n-now it just...sm--smells bad and is ch-changing colors.

TIME TO STOP FEELING SORRY FOR YOURSELF, MY MAN. I GOT THE WORD. THEY'RE GOING TO FIND YOU.

I-I DON'T BELIEVE IT.

THE PEQUOD PICKED UP A FAINT SIGNAL. YOU SHOULD BE EATING SOME GOOD, WHOLESOME **MUSH** WITHIN' THE HOUR.

HA! I--THANK YOU, MAN. I WAS **SURE** I WAS **DEAD.**

KING, I NEED TO-- BEFORE I GO, THERE'S SOMETHING I NEED TO DO.

AH-AH, MY FRIEND. **FIRST** WE GET YOU OUT OF HERE. SHE'LL KEEP.

THE STREETS ARE HOT RIGHT NOW. WE NEED TO GET YOU OUT OF SIGHT....

COME ON--

CLANK

RUSTLE RUSTLE

?

OH...CRAP...

RUN!

?

HI.

ZZ-- ZZZ

HOLY

YOUR FACE?... LORD, ROCKET, I THOUGHT YOU LOOKED SICK.... ARE YOU DYING?

NO, NO. IT'S ALL GOING TO BE OKAY NOW. IT'S GOING TO BE **WONDERFUL**! I'M GOING TO GET YOU OUT OF HERE, MONA. I'M GOING TO SAVE US BOTH.

ROCKET, I KNOW YOU'RE IN SOME KIND OF TROUBLE, BUT I DON'T CARE WHAT YOU'VE DONE. I'LL GO ANYWHERE WITH YOU. **ANYWHERE**! YOU CAN TRUST ME, ROCKET. **I SWEAR**!

I KNOW.....MONA, THERE ARE THINGS I CAN'T TELL YOU ABOUT JUST YET...ABOUT THE WORLD. BUT I KNOW THAT I **LOVE YOU**, AND THAT'S **REAL**. MORE REAL THAN ANYTHING I'VE EVER TOUCHED OR HELD IN MY OWN HANDS... I HAVE TO GO FOR A LITTLE WHILE, BUT I'LL BE BACK FOR YOU SOON. I PROMISE.

I'LL WAIT FOR YOU!

BRRRING!

THAT'S FOR ME.

ROCKET, BE CAREFUL. THE FBI'S LOOKING FOR YOU. A MAN CAME TO THE HOUSE.

A MAN?

I SAID I HADN'T SEEN YOU IN MONTHS.

WHAT DID HE LOOK LIKE!

OWW! ROCKET!

BRRRING!

ZZT

NO. NO!

ZZZ

RRROCKET!

STOP!

BRRRRING!

MONA!

ZZZ

115

THE END

THE MILLER'S TALE

STORY & ART BY PAUL CHADWICK

American writer and artist Paul Chadwick is most well known for his work on the critically acclaimed comic series CONCRETE, published by Dark Horse Comics since 1986. Other works by Paul include DEAD POOL, issue numbers 46 to 48, THE WORLD BELOW, a four issue series published from March to June 1999, and GIFTS OF THE NIGHT. In addition to writing several stories for Dark Horse's STAR WARS line, Chadwick will be returning to his signature character Concrete with a new six-part miniseries THE HUMAN DILEMMA, currently scheduled for release in the fall of 2003.

THE BOY WAITS. IT IS PART OF THE **DISCIPLINE**.

ZION IS A **PLACE** OF DISCIPLINE, SINCE IT WILL TAKE A GREAT DEAL TO DEFEAT THE POWER OF THE **MATRIX**.

SO HE REMAINS **UNMOVING**, THOUGH **EVERY MUSCLE** YEARNS TO **SQUIRM** AND **FLEX**.

YET THE SUPPRESSED AGITATION IS NOT **ANXIETY**, BUT ITS **OBVERSE**: **EXCITEMENT**, AND **JOY**.

STILL, TIME **STRETCHES** AS ALL ASSEMBLED ARE TOLD, IN ACCORDANCE WITH RITUAL, A **STORY**...

THE • MILLER'S • TALE
BY PAUL CHADWICK

HIS NAME WAS **GEOFFREY**.

HE WAS ONE OF THE **EARLIEST** LIBERATED FROM THE **MATRIX**.

MANY OF YOU KNOW THE **TRAUMA**, THE **DISAPPOINTMENT** OF THAT TRANSITION.

FOR WHILE FREEDOM IS A PRECIOUS GIFT, IT COMES AT **GREAT PRICE**...

...A COST OF SECURITY, OF COMFORT, OF **ILLUSION**.

LIFE, **REAL LIFE**, WAS EVEN HARSHER IN THOSE DAYS.

EDITED BY SPENCER LAMM   BASED ON CONCEPTS BY LARRY & ANDY WACHOWSKI

WE RAIDED THE SURFACE WORLD FOR WHAT WE NEEDED.

OFTEN, THOSE WHO WENT NEVER CAME BACK.

FORAYS INTO THE **MATRIX** WERE NO LESS HAZARDOUS. WE HAD **MUCH TO LEARN.**

AND THOSE WHO **SURVIVED** THESE RIGORS FENDED OFF **STARVATION** WITH THE PROTEIN-RICH **PORRIDGE** WE STILL USE TODAY.

ANOTHER BOWL OF THIS AND I'M GONNA **PUKE.**

I ALREADY **DID.**

I'VE GOT THE BOWL YOU **CAUGHT** IT IN.

LIFE WAS BLEAK. BUT THE WAR, AND SURVIVAL, WERE TOO **DESPERATE** FOR TIME TO BE GIVEN OVER TO THE PURSUIT OF **COMFORT.**

BUT IN A SURFACE FORAY, GEOFFREY CAME ACROSS SOMETHING NEW, OR, RATHER, SOMETHING **OLD.**

DISKS, SO PRIMITIVE THAT THEY CARRIED NO MORE DATA, THAN, SAY, A MATRIX AGENT'S HAIR, STIRRED BY A **VIRTUAL BREEZE.**

THEY CONTAINED **MOVIES.**

ONE MOVIE CAPTURED GEOFFREY'S FANCY.

IT DWELT LESS ON TWISTS OF PLOT, ON THE ENDLESS FASCINATION OF HUMAN INTERACTION, THAN DID MOST FILMS.

INSTEAD, IT CARESSED ITS IMAGERY, AND, IN THE MIDST OF A STORY, MADE SCENERY AND GENTLE, VAST SPECTACLE ITS FOCUS.

THE PRINCIPAL OCCUPATION OF ITS CHARACTERS WAS SOMETHING STRANGE TO GEOFFREY...

...THE CULTIVATION, AND HARVEST, OF WHEAT.

THE LOCUSTS THAT PLAGUED THEM REMINDED HIM OF THE INSECTILE MACHINES WE STILL BATTLE TODAY.

BUT WHAT STIRRED GEOFFREY SO WAS THE REPEATED IMAGE OF VAST FIELDS OF WHEAT.

... SUNLIT...

... WAVING IN THE BREEZE...

THIS BECAME A SYMBOL FOR HIM, AN EMBLEM THAT WARMED HIM...

... A VISION OF A SORT OF HEAVEN, DAYS LONG AGO, BUT, SHOULD HUMANS EVER DEFEAT THE ENEMY, PERHAPS DAYS AHEAD, AS WELL.

WHEAT WAS THE THING.

HE'D HAD "BREAD" AS A CHILD IN THE MATRIX, OF COURSE, BUT COULDN'T REMEMBER ITS TASTE.

PERHAPS THE ARTIFICIAL INTELLIGENCE BEHIND IT LACKED DATA ON ITS FLAVOR.

BUT SURELY, THE PRODUCT OF SUCH GOLDEN FIELDS MUST HAVE TASTED WONDERFUL.

GEOFFREY BEGAN TO RESEARCH WHEAT, AND BREAD, ONCE CALLED "THE STAFF OF LIFE" FOR MUCH OF HUMANITY.

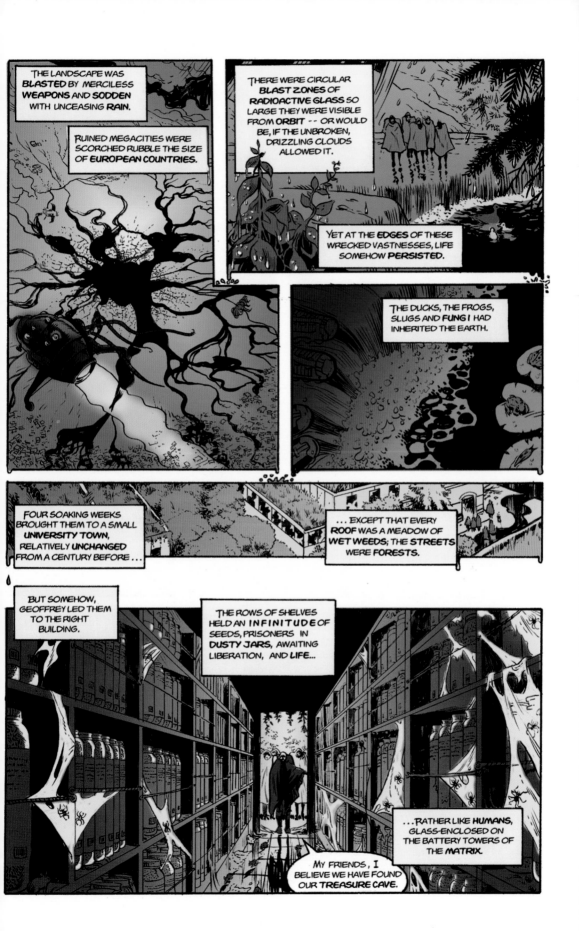

THE LANDSCAPE WAS **BLASTED** BY **MERCILESS WEAPONS** AND **SODDEN** WITH UNCEASING **RAIN**.

RUINED MEGACITIES WERE SCORCHED RUBBLE THE SIZE OF **EUROPEAN** COUNTRIES.

THERE WERE CIRCULAR **BLAST ZONES** OF **RADIOACTIVE GLASS** SO LARGE THEY WERE VISIBLE FROM **ORBIT** -- OR WOULD BE, IF THE UNBROKEN, DRIZZLING CLOUDS ALLOWED IT.

YET AT THE **EDGES** OF THESE WRECKED VASTNESSES, LIFE SOMEHOW **PERSISTED**.

THE DUCKS, THE FROGS, SLUGS AND **FUNGI** HAD INHERITED THE EARTH.

FOUR SOAKING WEEKS BROUGHT THEM TO A SMALL **UNIVERSITY TOWN**, RELATIVELY **UNCHANGED** FROM A CENTURY BEFORE ...

... EXCEPT THAT EVERY **ROOF** WAS A MEADOW OF **WET WEEDS**; THE **STREETS** WERE **FORESTS**.

BUT SOMEHOW, GEOFFREY LED THEM TO THE RIGHT BUILDING.

THE ROWS OF SHELVES HELD AN **INFINITUDE** OF SEEDS, PRISONERS IN **DUSTY JARS**, AWAITING LIBERATION, AND **LIFE** ...

... RATHER LIKE **HUMANS**, GLASS-ENCLOSED ON THE BATTERY TOWERS OF THE **MATRIX**.

MY FRIENDS, I BELIEVE WE HAVE FOUND OUR **TREASURE CAVE**.

123

THEY STUFFED THEIR PACKS AS IF WITH *BLOOD* FOR A *CRITICAL OPERATION.*

THEY DRIED OUT.

THEY *EXULTED* IN THEIR *SUCCESS.*

AND THEY GOT *SCARED.*

THE TRIP BACK WAS *LONG*, AND NOW THERE WAS *MUCH TO LOSE.*

THEIR FEARS WERE JUSTIFIED.

A *SURFACE SEEKER* FOUND THEM, AND THOUGH THEY FOUGHT HARD, IT WAS NO CONTEST.

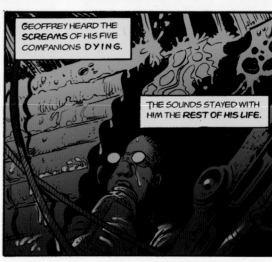

GEOFFREY HEARD THE *SCREAMS* OF HIS FIVE COMPANIONS *DYING.*

THE SOUNDS STAYED WITH HIM THE *REST OF HIS LIFE.*

IT MADE FAILURE IMPOSSIBLE. THEY COULD NOT DIE IN VAIN.

BUT A DOZEN FAILURES FOLLOWED.

THEN, SUCCESS.

HE MILLED THE SEEDS BY HAND, MIXED DOUGH...

...THE MOMENT CAME.

HE PRESENTED A HANDFUL OF *UNLEAVENED, DRY, COARSE, BURNT* LOAVES.

THE VERDICT WAS *UNANIMOUS.*

THEY WERE *MAGNIFICENT!*

ALONG A STILL-HOT LINE OF ELECTRICAL TOWERS, FAR FROM ANY CITY, THEY SET UP TENTS AGAINST THE RAIN.

DRAWING FROM THE LINES, A *THOUSAND ULTRAVIOLET LIGHTS* GLOWED IN THE DRY SPACE BELOW.

IT WORKED. PROBLEMS CAME AND WERE OVERCOME, AND THE CHILDREN OF ZION ATE BREAD.

YEARS PASSED.

MANY TRIPS TO THE SURFACE LEFT THEIR MARK.

BUT THE ENTERPRISE GREW, AS DID THE SKILL OF THE FARMERS AND BAKERS.

LIFE WAS NOT EASY, NO...

...BUT AWAITING THOSE RETURNING FROM *DESPERATE TRAVELS* TO THE SURFACE, OR TO THE *MATRIX ITSELF*...

...WAS THE SMELL OF FRESH-BAKED BREAD.

THE DELICIOUS IRONY WAS THAT WE WERE USING THE MATRIX'S *OWN POWER!*

POWER IS ALWAYS LOST IN TRANSMISSION, THROUGH **LINE FRICTION.**

FOR YEARS, OUR PILLAGE WENT *UNNOTICED.*

BUT NOT FOREVER.

NO HUMAN SURVIVED THE **BATTLE** OF THE **WHEAT FIELDS.**

WE ONLY KNOW WHAT HAPPENED BY **HACKING RECORDINGS** THE ATTACK MACHINES MADE.

WE KNOW THE FARMERS FOUGHT WITH **FIRE** AND **PRIDE.**

WOULD THAT WE ALL *DIE SO WELL.*

THEIR BONES LIE IN THE FIELD WHERE THEY FELL.

THE MACHINES, IT SEEMED, DEEMED IT TOO **COSTLY** TO CARRY BODIES BACK TO **LIQUEFACTION FACILITIES.**

SURELY THAT FIELD'S WATER-LOVING PLANTS ARE FULL OF THEIR SUBSTANCE.

NOW, TWICE A YEAR, WE TAKE A PORTION OF **STOCKPILED GRAIN,** AND HOLD A **BREAD FEAST.**

LET US ALL REMEMBER **GEOFFREY** AND HIS COMPATRIOTS, WHO SACRIFICED **SO MUCH** FOR WHAT WE ENJOY THIS DAY.

THIS IS THE SIGNAL TO EAT. BUT THERE IS NO RUSH, NO GRABBING.

IT IS TOO GOOD **NOT** TO SAVOR THIS MOMENT.

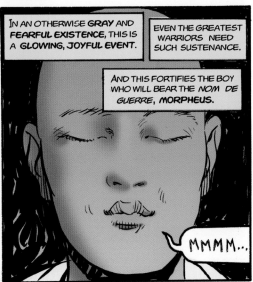

IN AN OTHERWISE **GRAY** AND **FEARFUL EXISTENCE,** THIS IS A **GLOWING, JOYFUL EVENT.**

EVEN THE GREATEST WARRIORS NEED SUCH SUSTENANCE.

AND THIS FORTIFIES THE BOY WHO WILL BEAR THE *NOM DE GUERRE,* MORPHEUS.

MMMM...

ARTISTIC FREEDOM

TWELVE MELVINS.

ART BY KILIAN
PLUNKETT

Since breaking into the comics industry with the art chores on ALIENS: LABYRINTH for Dark Horse, Kilian Plunkett became known for his uncanny skill at rendering facial likenesses, landing assignments on licensed comics based on SMALLVILLE and STAR WARS. While continuing to do art for the STAR WARS property Kilian's mainstream assignments have included the DC Comics Elseworlds title SUPERMAN: RED SON as well as an upcoming run on the JUSTICE LEAGUE series for DC.

Ryder and Kilian previously collaborated on the comic book mini-series TROUBLE MAGNET: THE ADVENTURES OF WITLOCK THE ROBOT (DC Comics), and the critically-acclaimed story "Thank the Maker" for STAR WARS TALES (Dark Horse Comics). They threaten to work together again when you least expect it.

COLOR BY JEROMY
COX

After a stint as a lead animator on several Saturday morning cartoons, Jeromy Cox, a four-time Eisner Award nominee, moved to Angel Studios to art direct a theme park attraction for DisneyQuest and an exhibit for the 1998 World's Fair, entitled Oceanus . A former senior art director and colorist for Wildstorm Studios, Jeromy's coloring credits include work on such award-winning comics as Leave It To Chance, Mage, Promethea, Teen Titans and Grendel. When he has time, he works on his own independent film, Gothic Cowboy.

THE MATRIX

ARTISTIC FREEDOM

STORY: RYDER WINDHAM
ART: KILIAN PLUNKETT
COLOR: JEROMY COX
EDITS: SPENCER LAMM & ROB SIMPSON
BASED ON CONCEPTS CREATED BY
ANDY AND LARRY WACHOWSKI

HEY, ART LOVERS! I'M *KITT PRITCHARD* WITH *CHANNEL 11 CULTURE BEAT...*

... AND WE'RE *LIVE* AT *HEDNET GALLERY* ON OPENING NIGHT FOR THE CONTROVERSIAL "NIGHTMARE SCULPTOR," *RAVEN UNDERWELL!*

UNDERWELL HAS MADE A *FORTUNE* FROM HER DARK VISIONS OF HUMANITY ENSLAVED BY MECHANICAL MONSTERS...

... AND SHE'S NOT THE ONLY ONE MAKING MONEY! PSYCHOLOGISTS ARE OVERWHELMED WITH PATIENTS WHO BLAME UNDERWELL'S SCULPTURES FOR THEIR SLEEPLESS NIGHTS!

COULD IT BE THAT THIS ARTIST'S WORK IS HAZARDOUS TO YOUR MENTAL HEALTH?

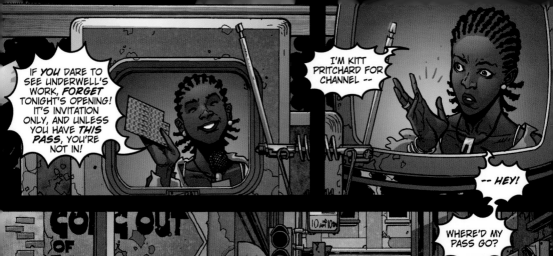

IT WAS A WORLD OF GIGANTIC TOWERS THAT WERE LIT UP LIKE CHRISTMAS TREES.

I LOOKED FOR SIGNS OR MARKERS, BUT THERE WAS NOTHING.

THE SKY WAS DARK AS A CAVE, WITHOUT ANY STARS. THEN THERE WAS THE SMELL.

WHEN I WAS A CHILD, MY COUSIN ONCE LEFT HIS ELECTRIC TOY TRAIN ON FOR TOO LONG. THAT'S WHAT IT SMELLED LIKE: A HOT TRANSFORMER, ONLY MORE INTENSE.

FOR A MOMENT, I WAS AFRAID. THEN I SAW THE SOMNICULTOS.

IT IS NOT ENOUGH TO BELIEVE WHAT YOU SEE. YOU MUST ALSO UNDERSTAND WHAT YOU SEE.

WHAT? WHO IS THIS?

WHAT AM I SUPPOSED TO UNDERSTAND?

OH, MY GOD.

CARETAKERS.

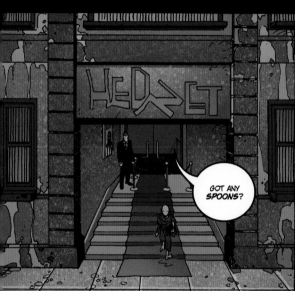

HUNTERS AND
COLLECTORS

STORY & ART BY GREGORY
RUTH

Greg Ruth's versatility is seen within the three Matrix stories he's done, and also on display in M.A.R.S. and SUDDEN GRAVITY. For the New York Transit Museum, Greg also produced an installation series of eleven murals that were displayed in the heart of NYC Grand Central Terminal for the 2002 winter season. His latest offering is the five part mini-series FREAKS OF THE HEARTLAND, in conjunction with writer Steve Niles.

THEY CALLED HIM *AHAB*.

THE POLARIS IS LOADED AND READY, FLINT-

WE NEED TO *GO*. TWIST IS TRACKING A *SQUIDDY* IN OUR VICINITY...

BUT YOU *KNEW* THAT ALREADY.

LOOK, FLINT...

NO ONE SURVIVES A CON-FRONTATION WITH A SENTINEL.

WHAT HAPPENED TO THE PEQUOD *WASN'T* YOUR FAULT -

I'LL SEE YOU BACK AT ZION, NOVA.

I LET THE SHIP GO AND FOLLOWED HIM, UNINVITED, INTO THE UNEXPLORED ENDS OF THE CITY.

I ASKED FLINT ABOUT THIS, BUT HE REFUSED ANY CONVERSATION, AND I KNEW HIM WELL ENOUGH NOT TO PRESS.

THIS WASN'T JUST SOME CASUAL GESTURE, BUT AN EX-AMPLE OF MY TOTAL FAITH IN HIM.

YOU SEE, FLINT WAS THE FIRST OF US. THE FIRST *COLLECTOR*.

AS CHILDREN WE HEARD ENDLESS TALES TOLD IN HUSHED REVERENCE OF HIS EXPEDITIONS- BRAVING *SENTINELS*, SURVIVING FOR *WEEKS* IN THE CITIES- ALL TO COLLECT THE BROKEN REMNANTS OF HUMAN HISTORY.

THERE WERE *OTHER* STORIES TOO...

...TALES I TRIED HARD TO FORGET AS WE MARCHED PAST THE VERY ARTIFACTS WE WERE MEANT TO BE GATHERING

MANY SAID HE'D *CHANGED* SINCE HE LOST THE PEQUOD AND ITS CREW TO A SENTINEL ATTACK LAST YEAR-

-THEY SAY IT DROVE HIM MAD; THAT ALL HE SOUGHT OUT NOW WAS REVENGE, AND *DEATH*.

I WOULDN'T.

I COULDN'T LET MYSELF BELIEVE *ANY* OF IT.

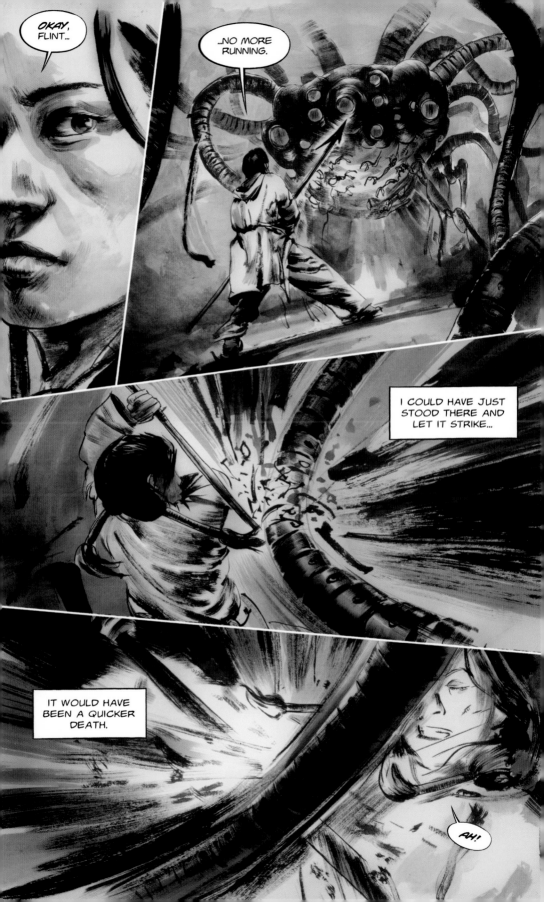

WITHOUT AN *APU* OR SO MUCH AS A *LIGHTENING GUN*, NO ONE HAD EVER ATTEMPTED WHAT FLINT JUST DIED DOING.

AND NOW, WHAT I WAS ATTEMPTING.

BUT I COULD NOT TURN AWAY.

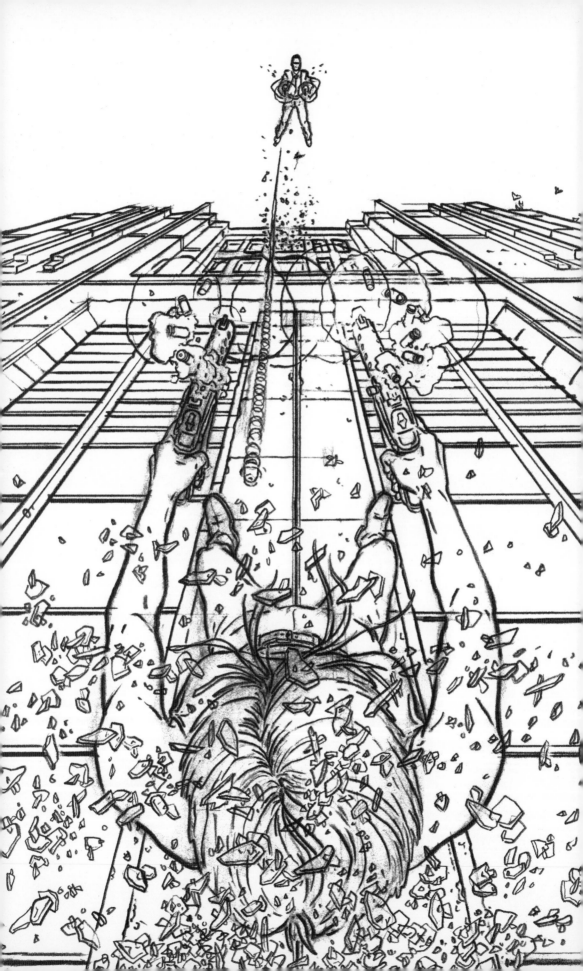

THE ART OF THE
MATRIX
RELOADED REVOLUTIONS

Hundreds of storyboards,
conceptual illustrations and photos.

Artist and crew commentaries throughout.

COMING IN 2004

Designed by the same team behind THE ART OF THE MATRIX.

THE WACHOWSKI BROTHERS PRESENT

ACTION!! Served the way we like it — fresh heaping stinking body-count mounting piles of it! From our new line of burly barrel-chested entertainment

STEVE SKROCE

GEOF DARROW

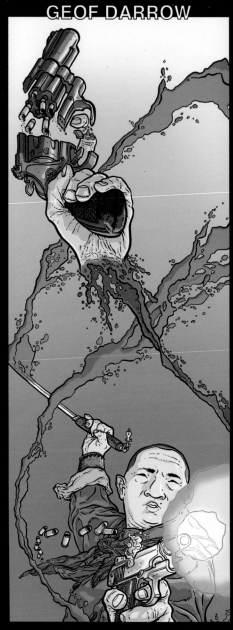

DOC FRANKENSTEIN
UNHOLY NEMESIS OF EVIL
CREATED BY
GEOF DARROW • STEVE SKROCE

HE HAS NO PAST...
HE HAS NO FUTURE...
BUT HE HAS PLENTY OF AMMUNITION!

The SHAOLIN COWBOY
created by Geof Darrow

COMING TO BOOKSTORES 2004
FROM BURLYMAN ENTERTAINMENT